WELCOME!

Come in, friends. The door is open. Won't you sit down? No, no, no! Not there! Sit by the fire . . . let the bristling flames warm you. It is chilly in here . . . as if the cold air of death were in the room! Here, we'll stoke the coals. Ah, the fire leaps up with a thousand fingers as its nails of white heat slash at our flesh—like the ripping fangs of a werewolf downing its screaming victim under a blood-red full moon!

Do the torture racks along the walls frighten you? Don't cower in front of those skeletons. They're old friends! You ask what ghastly ghouls has this room seen? What horrible terror will the room see? The answers would make the eyes of a human man pivot with fear in their sockets. They would sear his sanity as burning pokers! All the stories we are about to tell you are true . . . or don't you believe in witches, ghouls and ghosts. . . WE DO!

The stories you will read will turn your veins into tiny bands of ice as you delve into the mystery of murder, the savageness of the supernatural and the viciousness of vampires! The stories you will read will make your scalp crawl when the dead dig their claws into living flesh! You . . .

SLAM!!!

The door is closed! The demons are ready! Clutch your chair! You are trapped in the . . .

CHAMBER OF CHILLS

CHAMBER OF CHILLS MAGAZINE, JUNE, 1951, Vol. 1, No. 21, IS PUBLISHED EVERY OTHER MONTH by WITCHES TALES, INC., 1860 Broadway, New York 23, N.Y. Application for second class entry pending at the Post Office at New York, N.Y. under the Act of March 3, 1879. Single copies 10c. Subscription rates, 10 issues for $1.00 in the U.S. and possessions, elsewhere $1.50. All names in this periodical are entirely fictitious and no identification with actual persons is intended. Contents copyrighted, 1951, by Witches Tales, Inc., New York City.
Printed in the U.S.A.

MIKE!! IT IS *YOU!!* WH... WHAT HAS *HAPPENED* TO YOU?!

THOMAS...THOMAS, MY FRIEND...YOU ARE TALKING TO A DEAD MAN—ONLY THE RESTLESS AND DOOMED SPIRIT OF MIKE NOONAN SPEAKS!

AND THAT'S MY STORY, THOMAS... DOOMED... DOOMED...

IT...IT'S INCREDIBLE! BUT I'M GLAD I FOUND YOU, THAT I CAME LOOKING FOR YOU. THERE MUST BE SOME WAY I CAN HELP YOU! EH! WHAT WAS THAT?

HEE-HEE-HEEEE! LISTEN TO THE FOOLISH MORTAL, SATAN!

PURRRRRR...

LISTEN, EVIL ONE! I AM A MAN OF GOD—AND IN THE NAME OF THE GOOD BOOK, THE BANISHER OF EVIL SPIRITS, I DEMAND YOU RELEASE MICHAEL NOONAN FROM YOUR UNJUST CURSE! SPEAK!

NO...NO!! COME NO CLOSER TO ME! YOU MUST HANG HIM...HANG HIM...

SPPST!

KEEP BACK... KEEP BACK...KEEP BAAAAAAAHHHHH!

MEWOOORRR! SPSSST! SPSST!

PEACE BE WITH YOU, EVIL ONE! MAY THERE BE MERCY EVEN FOR YOU!

DO NOT GRIEVE, THOMAS. I AM BODILY ALREADY DEAD—IT IS MY SPIRIT WHICH YOU MUST HELP ME LAY AT REST. I AM WEARY, THOMAS... WEARY! NOW YOU MUST HELP ME DO THE DEED...GOODBYE...

GOODBYE, OLD FRIEND...

THE END

THE AVENGING SPECTRE!

The roulette wheel spun around and around. When it stopped . . .

"I won! I won again!"

The group around the table began to laugh and clap. Cyrus Watson had won again. With this winning, he will have broken the bank of the Lamont Gambling Casino.

Jock Lamont, owner of the Club, stepped over to Watson.

"Well, Mr. Watson, you've cleaned us out, to-night. Sorry, folks, but the bank is closed!"

Lamont spun around and headed for his private office. When he was seated in his huge, oaken chair, he pressed a button.

"Ripper, Johnnie, c'mere, quick!"

In a few minutes, the door to Lamont's office swung open and in strode two killers.

"What gives boss? snapped the man with the ugly scar gashing his left cheek.

"Ripper, a sucker has taken us! We tried all of the phony stuff on him but he still won. You boys know what I want you to do. And, to make sure you do it right, I'm coming with you!"

Later that evening, as Cyrus Watson left the casino, three men piled into a car and began to trail Watson's car. Then, suddenly, the car following Watson's swerved out in front and stopped dead.

The three men ran from their car, flung the door to Watson's car open and dragged Watson out!

"Wait, wait," pleaded Watson, "you can't kill me. Here, I'll give you the money. Don't! If you shoot me, I swear my brother will avenge my death. My brother . . ."

BAM! BAM! BAM!

"Okay Johnnie, Ripper, let's get out of here. We'll spend a few days up at my lodge!"

* *

"Mr. Lamont," snapped Ripper, "we been up at this lodge for four days now. I'm getting the creeps. Remember what that guy said about his brother!"

"Dry up, Ripper, or I'll cleave your skull with this bottle!"

"Shut up, the two of you," blasted Lamont. "I've checked Watson's brother and he was hung ten years ago on a frame-up we worked!"

"Hey, what happened to the lights?" Ripper gasped.

Then, as the men groped about in the dark, they heard a gurgled scream, the end of which seemed to die in a *human throat*.

"Say, there go the lights on, again," Johnnie yelled but his yell instantly turned into a sigh of horror. On the floor, his neck broken by a thick cord, lay Ripper!

"Boss, that dead guy's curse is coming true. It got Ripper. I'm gonna get out of here!"

"Stay right where you are, Johnnie. Something funny is going on. We'll barricade ourselves in and then let any ghost try to get us." Jock Lamont scowled as he began to prepare a plan to keep them alive!

After the men had set up a complicated defense system of alarms and traps, they waited . . . waited for something unknown!

At about eleven o'clock that night, a soft knock was heard. "Boss, somebody's outside. What'll we do?" whispered Johnnie.

"It's okay. I called for some of the boys to come up and give us a hand. Open the door," ordered Lamont.

As Johnnie went to the door, Lamont turned his back and lit a cigarette.

"Well, where are you, Johnnie?" impatiently called Lamont after a few minutes had passed and no one came. Crushing the cigarette in his palm, the gang leader walked over to the door and threw it open. His eyes bulged . . . as Johnnie's were bulging except Johnnie was sprawled on the ground, strangled!

Stumbling back inside, Lamont slammed the door shut. His fingers, sweating bands of flesh, dug into the door.

Lamont wasn't a man anymore. He was the beast in the jungle, wounded and cornered. With desperation, Jock Lamont whipped out his gun and began to scream:

"I ain't afraid of you! Come on! You'll never get me!"

As the shadow of a man and a noose hanging from his hands fell over Lamont, the revolver dropped from the crook's limp fingers.

Lamont couldn't even move as the rope slipped around his neck. What he saw and what was happening to him had frozen him into a living corpse!

IT CAME TOWARD HIM – BLACKER THAN MIDNIGHT – MORE TERRIBLE THAN A NIGHTMARE!! HOW COULD A MAN FIGHT THAT WHICH WOULD NOT DIE! THE THING THAT WAS...

DARKER THAN DEATH!

CAL HODGINS WAS AN EASY-GOING SOUL – TOO MUCH SO FOR HIS AMBITIOUS WIFE. HE AMBLED ALL OVER NEW ENGLAND WITH HIS HARDWARE STORE ON WHEELS. THO' HE DIDN'T MAKE MUCH MONEY, HE LIKED WONDERING ABOUT WHAT THE NEXT DAY WOULD BRING...

NOW WHICH WAY DO WE GO, CAL... RIGHT OR LEFT?

MAKES NO DIFFERENCE, JANET. NEVER BEEN THROUGH THIS PART BEFORE.

FATE MUST HAVE BEEN LAUGHING THAT DAY AS JANET TOOK ONE OF THE FORKS. SOMETIMES A STRANGE ROAD LEADS TO A STRANGE END...

HEY, OLD-TIMER – COULD YOU HELP A STRANGER OUT AND TELL ME WHERE THIS ROAD GOES?

SURE, SON – IT GOES STRAIGHT TO DEATH – THAT'S WHERE IT GOES!

HEY, WHAT DO YOU *MEAN*, POP?

MISTER, IF I HAD MY WAY, I'D *BLOCK* THIS ROAD OFF SO NO HUMAN BEING COULD GO DOWN IT! THIS ROAD LEADS TO THE OLD RANDALL HOUSE... *AND DEATH.!!!*

SON, THIS IS THE *THIRD* MAN I'VE *BURIED* IN THE LAST TEN YEARS—AND EVERY DANG ONE OF THEM *STAYED* AT THE RANDALL PLACE! YOU SHOULD HAVE SEEN WHAT THEY LOOKED LIKE...UGH... TOO *HORRIBLE* TO DESCRIBE!

CAL! CAL! CAL HODGINS! OH, THAT MAN! HE'S *WORSE* THAN AN OLD WOMAN—HAS TO HEAR ALL THE LOCAL GOSSIP!

DADDY... DADDY...

ALL RIGHT, BOYS...*HURRY* IT UP! FEELS LIKE A STORM'S COMING! SO, YOU WANT THE WHOLE STORY, EH! OKAY, I'LL *TELL* IT TO YOU!

FINE!! GO AHEAD, SHERIFF!

"*A*BOUT TEN YEARS AGO, WHEN I WAS FIRST ELECTED SHERIFF, OLD MAN RANDALL AND HIS NEPHEW LIVED IN THE HOUSE. RANDALL WAS THE RICHEST MAN IN THE STATE— AND THE *STINGIEST*..."

YOU'RE *DYING*, UNCLE -- I'VE *POISONED* YOUR WINE! NOW YOUR FORTUNE WILL BE MINE -- *ALL MINE!!*

...ARRGH...YOU'LL NEVER....(GASP)... GET IT, JOHN... (GASP)...NOT A RED PENNY... I'VE HIDDEN IT.... AGHHHHHH...

"THE OLD MAN WAS MY FRIEND, AND WHEN I DIDN'T SEE HIM FOR A FEW DAYS, I RODE OUT TO THE MANSION. WHEN I GOT THERE I FOUND HIM..."

DEAD.!! POOR OLD RANDALL— HE ALWAYS TOLD ME HE NEVER TRUSTED THAT *NEPHEW* OF HIS...

JOHN DID IT

"WE *NEVER* DID FIND THE OLD MAN'S NEPHEW... JUST DISAPPEARED. ANYHOW, WE BOARDED THE HOUSE UP. PEOPLE AROUND HERE KEPT AWAY FROM IT...BUT, EVERY ONCE IN A WHILE..."

GUESS I CAN STAY *HERE* TILL MORNIN'! BOY, AM I *TIRED*!

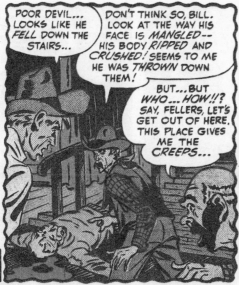

"HE WAS THE *FIRST* ONE! I WENT OUT TO INSPECT THE MANSION AND FOUND HIM... *DEAD!* THEN, I FOUND *TWO* MORE OF 'EM! THE THIRD ONE, WE'VE JUST *BURIED.* THE FUNNY THING IS THAT THEY ALL *DIED* IN THE SAME *BLOOD-CHILLIN'* WAY!"

POOR DEVIL... LOOKS LIKE HE *FELL* DOWN THE STAIRS...

DON'T THINK SO, BILL. LOOK AT THE WAY HIS FACE IS *MANGLED*-- HIS BODY *RIPPED* AND *CRUSHED!* SEEMS TO ME HE WAS *THROWN* DOWN THEM!

BUT... BUT *WHO*.... *HOW!!?* SAY, FELLERS, LET'S GET OUT OF HERE. THIS PLACE GIVES ME THE *CREEPS...*

AND YOU NEVER FOUND OUT HOW THEY DIED... OR WHAT KILLED THEM?

NO! THIS LAST ONE HAD *NO FACE LEFT!*--AND *NO IDENTIFICATION!* BUT EVERY ONE WHO HAS STAYED IN THAT HOUSE ONE NIGHT HAS DIED A *HORRIBLE DEATH!* THE SECOND FELLA WE FOUND IN *THREE PIECES!*

UNKNOWN

WELL, IT'S ABOUT TIME!

THANKS, POP, FOR TELLING ME THAT *STORY.* I WOULDN'T MIND TAKING A *LOOK* AT THE OLD PLACE!

TAKE MY *ADVICE,* SON, AND JUST TURN YOUR WAGON AROUND IF IT RAINS, IT WOULDN'T DO YOUR FAMILY ANY *GOOD* TO BE CAUGHT OUTSIDE!

CAL, THE OLD MAN SAID TO TURN *BACK*--AND THOSE STORM CLOUDS ARE PILING UP!

I GOT TO SEE THIS OLD PLACE, JANET... IT'S *ONLY* A FEW MILES DOWN THE ROAD! GID-UP THAR!

*B*UT CAL WAS AS *CURIOUS* AS HE WAS CAREFREE. HE WAS DRAWN TOWARD THE OLD RANDALL PLACE AS A HOOKED FISH IS DRAWN TO THE FISHERMAN...

IT'S A *HORRIBLE* OLD PLACE, CAL-- IT LOOKS AS IF THE HOUSE ITSELF HAS SOME *TERRIBLE ROTTING DISEASE!*

FOUR MEN HAVE *DIED* IN THAT HOUSE... STRANGE...

I... I C...CAN'T (PUFF-PUFF) BUDGE THE WAGON!!

NOW YOU'VE DONE IT... AND THERE'S NOBODY AROUND FOR MILES!! OH, CAL--YOU *ARE* A FOOL! YOUR CURIOSITY WILL BE THE *DEATH* OF US YET!

I'M SCARED, MOMMY!

THE STORM SOUNDED AS IF *GIANTS* WERE BATTLING IN THE SKY. AS THE WET, FOGGY NIGHT CLOSED IN, THE *LONELY* EYE OF A NEARBY LIGHTHOUSE *WICKEDLY* WINKED ON AND OFF, GLARING AT THE *INTRUDERS*...

WELL, WE'RE *STUCK* FOR FAIR! LOOK, I'M GOING TO TAKE A GLANCE AROUND THE OLD HOUSE. MAYBE WE *COULD* MANAGE TO STAY FOR A NIGHT! NOW, DON'T WORRY, JANET, I'LL TAKE THE *GUN!* THERE ISN'T ANYTHING *LIVING* THAT WON'T *DIE* WHEN YOU *SHOOT* IT!

CR-E-E-EAK

C'MON, CAL, WHAT ARE YOU *AFRAID* OF? IT'S JUST AN *OLD, DESERTED HOUSE!* AND, YET...OH, GOOD... THERE'S A LANTERN...

THOUGH CAL DIDN'T KNOW EXACTLY WHY, *FEAR* TWISTED IN HIS STOMACH AND SENT A TINGLING SENSATION ACROSS HIS SCALP. SOME LOST, PRIMITIVE SENSE SEEMED TO BE WARNING HIM THAT HE WAS *NOT...ALONE!!!*

HEY? *WHAT* WAS *THAT?* SOUNDS LIKE *BATS...*

FLAP...
FLAP...

GOOD HEAVENS! *WHAT IS IT!*

BLAM!
BLAM!

THE *MONSTER* SWOOPED TOWARD HIM, EACH CLAW AS DANGEROUS, AS A HANDFUL OF KNIVES!! THEN HE FELT AS IF *HOT POKERS* HAD BEEN *RAMMED* INTO HIS FACE, WHEN...

A-A-A-A-H AH-H-H-H!

YOU *BLACK DEVIL!!* WHATEVER YOU ARE-- YOU'LL FEEL THE *POINT* OF MY *KNIFE* BEFORE I'M A *DEAD* MAN!

CAL KNEW HE WAS LOOKING *DEATH* IN THE FACE AS THE *WEIRD* SHAPE PREPARED TO ATTACK *AGAIN!* WEAK FROM LOSS OF BLOOD, CAL BECAME VERY DIZZY, BUT IN HIS SWEATY HAND HE HELD, TIGHTLY, HIS ONLY WEAPON AND HOPE...

AIEEEE!

AS THE KNIFE PLUNGED INTO THE BONY BREAST OF THE *EVIL THING*, A PIERCING SCREAM, HALF HUMAN, RIPPED THROUGH THE HOUSE. ENCOURAGED, CAL GRABBED THE THING BY ITS HEAD, AND...

WHATEVER YOU ARE, YOU CAN'T TAKE *COLD STEEL*...HEY!!

HELP ME... I... I'M *DYING*...

LOOK!!! WHO IS IT?

I THOUGHT I'D BETTER TAKE A LOOK OUT HERE WHEN YOU PEOPLE DIDN'T GET TO TOWN, AND I... WELL, I'LL BE A SOW'S EAR!! THAT'S *JOHN RANDALL!!!*

CAL-ARE YOU ALL RIGHT? THE *SHOTS!!*

BUT HE *FLEW!!* HOW COULD HE...?

LOOK UP THERE! THAT'S HOW! SON, YOU'VE GOT A REWARD COMING FOR THIS!

YES, I'VE BEEN HIDING HERE ALL THESE YEARS -- LOOKING FOR THE MONEY MY UNCLE HID... KEEPING OTHERS AWAY... ONE OF THE SHOTS CUT THE ROPE- THE OTHERS WENT THROUGH THE WINGS. DIDN'T HARM ME... *HA-HA-HA-AAAH!*

CAL, WILL YOU STOP COUNTING THAT REWARD MONEY AND TELL ME WHICH WAY TO GO?

...THREE HUNDRED, FOUR HUN... HUH? OH, TAKE ANY ONE, JANET- I'VE NEVER BEEN THROUGH THIS PART BEFORE!!!

The End

GORILLA!

"And that ends the five-thirty newscast. However, we repeat. A mad gorilla has broken loose from a traveling circus and is free in the vicinity of Melville. All residents of that area are warned to stay indoors! Your news reporter was . . ."

"Oh, I'm happy you turned the radio off, Bill. That report about the escaped gorilla was frightening me." Why, he's on the loose right here."

"Don't worry, Martha! They'll get him. The poor thing is probably scared to death."

The husband and wife went back to playing cards. Suddenly, they were snapped out of their game by the shouts of their little boy.

"Dad, Mom! Spots wants to come inside. I can hear him whining. Please let me bring him in!"

"Sure, go ahead, son," smiled the father.

"But, Bill, that animal is prowling around here," warned Martha.

"Oh, the dog is just out back. Danny'll be all right."

*   *

"Bill, Danny has been gone for a long time. Please go out and get him."

"You're right. He's probably having a hard time unhooking the dog's leash. We'll be right back."

*   *

"Now what happened to Bill," anxiously thought Martha. "It looks like I'll have to go out there and bring back *two* babies!"

Wrapping a shawl around her head, the woman opened the door and headed for the doghouse next to the well.

"That's strange. No one's here . . . Good heavens! I just heard a sound from the well."

Running over to the well, Martha thought that Danny had fallen in and her husband had gone down after him and now wanted help to get out. Plunging her arm into the black pit, Martha cried, "Here Bill, grab my arm!"

Horror ripped at the woman's heart as she felt a hard, hairy hand grip her's and start to pull her down!

Strange

HIS SKULL WILL DR
THE DEMONS FROM
GROUND AND MAKE IT

GHOS
MAY RIP
BODY EVEN

IN PARTS OF THE PHILIPPINES, THE NATIVES PRACTICE HEAD-HUNTING FOR AGRICULTURAL REASONS. THEY BELIEVE THAT IF THE CROP IS TO COME OUT RIGHT A SEVERED HUMAN HEAD MUST BE PRESENTED AT THE PLANTING AND THE SOWING...

THE GUNS
WHITE MEN
OFFENDED THE ST
LORDS OF THE JU

IN THE LANDS WHERE THE TIGER ROAMS FEARED AND FRE MANY OF THE NATIVES REFUSE TO HUNT THE ANIMAL. THE BELIEVE THAT IF ONE TIGER IS KILLED, TEN OF THEM WILL DIE UNDER THE FLASHING CLAWS OF OTHER TIGERS.

USTOMS

"COME, BROTHER, TO THE STAKE, TAKE THE ROBE. THERE IS A CHANCE THAT YOU WILL SURVIVE!"

...AT ...ORCERERS ...F A HUMAN ...ON HAS EVERY

IF THE LEADING CHIEFS OF THE SAVAGE TIMMES DON'T LIKE SOMEBODY, THEY GET RID OF HIM IN A VERY UNUSUAL WAY. THEY MAKE HIM KING! THIS GIVES THE TRIBE THE RIGHT OF BEATING HIM ON THE EVE OF HIS CORONATION. SUCH A BEATING IS USUALLY FATAL...

...E INHABITANTS OF THE CELEBES LAY THE BLAME UPON ...VILS WHEN A SIEGE OF SICKNESS GRIPS THEIR VILLAGES. ...FIGHT THIS SICKNESS, THE PEOPLE RUN UP AND DOWN THE ...EETS OF THE VILLAGES SCREAMING AND STRIKING THE ...ES THINKING THAT THE EVIL ONES WILL BE CHASED AWAY.

GRAY DEATH

The screaming wind tossed the little sailboat around on the foaming waves like a bobbing balloon. The sky was inky black with the approaching storm.

Tim and Barney struggled bravely to keep their little craft afloat.

Finally, after what seemed like eternities to the shivering men, the sailboat was driven into a tiny cove and was washed ashore on what appeared to be a small, rocky island.

"Tim!" Barney yelled suddenly, springing to his feet. "There's someone else here! See, there —in the mist? A man's shape!" He ran forward a little way, Tim close at his heels. There was no sound from the man in the mist.

"Are you all right?" Barney called anxiously. He put out his hand to the man—and screamed as the man's arm seemed to ooze right through his fingers! Then the silent figure moved closer —like an evil, slimy jellyfish. Frantically, the men tried to fight off the monstrous horror that surged around them like glue! But there was nothing they could grab! Their fists shot right through the gray mistiness of the man's figure, and came out cold and clammy—as if a spider had spun its web around them!

Suddenly there was a ripping noise—like the sound of rotted human flesh being torn away— and the man screamed in agony—the first sound he'd made during the whole terrible struggle! And from Barney's nerveless fingers dripped a blob of gray, sponge-like jelly!

"I only wanted to warn you away from this cursed island!" the misty figure shouted. "Everything here is covered with a sticky gray moss that YOU MUST NOT TOUCH! I was shipwrecked here a year ago . . . I was starving . . . Heaven help me . . . I tasted it . . . the gray stuff . . . and it was good! Until one day I noticed . . . on my leg . . . a little patch of gray . . ."

Their breaths sobbing in their throats, the terrified men turned and ran . . . flying from a nameless terror! With frantic haste, they cast off in the battered sailboat -neither one of them speaking until they'd put several miles between themselves and the island. And then Tim screamed—a high, wild wail of almost insane despair!

"Your leg!" Barney looked down at his bare knee. Clinging to it was an oozing patch of grayish jelly!

TRICKS to MYSTIFY YOUR FRIENDS

This is the trick of tricks! Can you reach into the air and pluck from it a wooden ball?

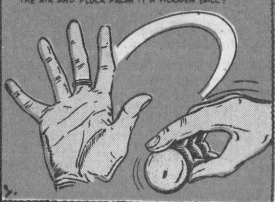

Divide a pack of cards into two portions. Take a card from one half and put it in the other. The magician, on examining the second half, can tell you what the card is. Dare you explain how?

Did you ever see a magician pull a tablecloth out from under a fully set table? Well, similarly, by placing a card on your right forefinger and a coin on top of this card, can you flip the card away and still have the coin balanced on your finger?

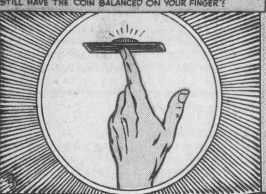

Here's a trick that should attract you! How is it possible to take a wooden checker and slap it against a wall so that the checker will stick to the wall?

You'll have to knuckle down to do this one, heh, heh! Let's see you rap your knuckles on the edge of a table and not have your face turn blue from the pain!

Solutions...

1. Wear a ring on the second finger of the right hand. Attach a string with a ball to this ring and have the ball hang down the back of the hand. Then, jerk the hand and catch the ball as it jumps up.

2. Have the halves so arranged that one portion has all odd cards - ace, nine, three, jack, etc. - while the other has all even cards. When you look through either portion, it will be quite easy to find the chosen card.

3. Use a very heavy coin. With your right forefinger, hit the card hard and it will sail away, leaving the coin on your finger.

4. Make sure the checker is smooth. When you slap it against the wall, slide it up a short distance, the friction will take care of the sticking.

5. Gently rap your knuckles a few times against a table edge as if you are practicing. Then, quickly start a blow for the table, letting the tips of your fingers hit the table. After the blow, redouble your fist and the people will think your knuckles actually struck the table.

THE WORLD TURNED IN SPACE MANY TIMES AS MABU GREW, BUT HE WAS TOUCHED BY EVIL, AND IN HIS BRAIN A SLOW POISON MADE HIM DO EVIL THINGS...

MABU, YOU *SON* OF *SATAN*, WHAT POSSESSES YOU TO DO THAT? YOUR FATHER SHALL HEAR ABOUT THIS!

FOOL! THE BOY *IS* POSSESSED! BUT, THIS IS *JUST* THE BEGINNING!

G-A-A-AWWKK!

WHY DO YOU LASH HIM? HE DOES WHAT YOU ORDER HIM.

QUIET! I'LL GIVE *YOU* SOMETHING TO SING ABOUT! I'LL LASH WHOM I PLEASE -- WHENEVER THE *SPIRIT* MOVES ME TO LASH!

A!EEEEEEE!

MY SON, I SAW WHAT YOU DID TO KEELA! *WHAT* HAS GOT *INTO YOU* TO MAKE YOU DO SUCH CRUELTY? NOW GIVE ME THAT WHIP!

SOMETIMES I LOSE MY HEAD, FATHER. I DON'T KNOW WHY! I JUST WANTED THEM TO BUILD ME A PLAY HOUSE...

HOW IS YOUR BACK, KEELA?

IT BURNS LIKE THE WOUND OF A POISON SNAKE! HOW LONG SHALL WE STAND HIS BULLYING?

MABU! I WARN YOU! LOOLA IS MY BETROTHED-- YOU HAVE NO RIGHT HERE! IT IS ALL ARRANGED BETWEEN OUR FAMILIES! BEGONE OR THERE WILL BE GREAT TROUBLE!

AH-- IT IS MY OLD PLAYMATE, KEELA! SILENCE, WEAK ONE! IT IS *I* WHO WILL CLAIM LOOLA!

FOR MANY YEARS YOU HAVE BROUGHT PAIN AND MISERY TO THE CREATURES OF THE WORLD. BUT ONLY OVER MY DEAD BODY WILL YOU BRING PAIN TO LOOLA!

YOU CHALLENGE ME, FOOL! YOU CHALLENGE *MABU*??

ALL RIGHT, I ACCEPT YOUR CHALLENGE, FOOL! THERE IS THE SIGN OF THE CROSSED SPEARS! TONIGHT, I WILL WET THE EARTH WITH YOUR BLOOD!

AWAY AND PRAY TO YOUR FIENDS FOR HELP! I HAVE LONG WISHED TO RID OUR ISLAND OF YOUR PRESENCE! TONIGHT, *YOU* DIE!

THE *FIENDS* WATCH OVER MABU! HEE-HEEEEE, DEATH *SHALL* COME THIS NIGHT...

YOU BOTH KNOW THE RULES! *ONLY THE DAGGER AND THE SHIELD, AND THE FIGHT CONTINUES UNTIL EITHER ONE YIELDS OR DIES!* READY?

KEELA MUST WIN -- HE IS HONORABLE! MABU HAD NO RIGHT TO GO TO THE HUT OF LOOLA. NOW MABU WILL PAY FOR HIS PAST WICKEDNESS! *KEELA... KEELA...*

THE TRIBE IS AGAINST MABU -- BUT THERE ARE THOSE WHO *CANNOT BE SEEN* AND WHO WILL HELP MABU!

PREPARE TO DIE, KEELA -- LOWER THAN THE SNAKE'S BELLY! THIS IS YOUR FUNERAL DAY!

LESS TALK AND MORE FIGHT! YOUR TONGUE IS SHARPER THAN YOUR KNIFE!

HERE... TAKE *THIS!*

YOU ARE OVER-ANXIOUS TO KILL MABU!

THUG!

TERROR FLASHED FROM MABU'S EYES AS THE POINT OF KEELA'S KNIFE INCHED TOWARD HIS THROAT...

YOU... ARE... DONE... MABU!! I GIVE YOU ONE CHANCE... TO... YIELD!

I... I... Y-YIELD TO YOU, KEELA...

OH, KEELA -- I WAS SO FRIGHTENED FOR YOU...

I ALWAYS KNEW HE WAS A BULLY -- *AFRAID* OF *DEATH...*

WHAT WILL YOU DO NOW, MABU? YOU ARE *DISGRACED* IN THE EYES OF THE PEOPLE, AND... HUH??

GIVE ME THAT STICK, OLD WOMAN! A MAN NEEDS A *STICK* RATHER THAN A *KNIFE* TO *KILL* A SNAKE!

KEELA!! LOOK OUT..!!

UH...

NO ONE LIVES TO GLOAT OVER MABU!

AFTER MABU MURDERED KEELA, HE RAN LIKE A HUNTED ANIMAL, TO ESCAPE THE FURY OF THE ANGRY VILLAGERS HE RAN DEEP INTO THE DARK JUNGLE, AND AS I KNEW HE WOULD, TO MY CAVE-FOR ALL THE WORLD KNOWS THAT *EVIL ATTRACTS EVIL...*

(GASP) I...I THINK I'VE LOST TH-THEM NOW... NOW...(PUFF-PUFF) BUT... OH!! OLD WOMAN- WHAT ARE *YOU* DOING HERE!

THIS IS MY HOME, MABU, FOR FIVE TIMES LONGER THAN YOU ARE OLD! I WAS THERE WHEN THE FIENDS MARKED YOU --AND NOW YOU HAVE COME TO THE RIGHT PLACE! SIT- THEY WILL NOT SEEK YOU HERE!

WHAT DO YOU MEAN BY SAYING THE *FIENDS* MARKED ME? OH- HOW I WISH I HAD THE *POWER* TO BEND THE VILLAGERS UNDER MY WILL! I WOULD MAKE THEM ALL *SWEAT* AND *SQUIRM!*

YOU HAVE THE POWER, MABU, WITH MY HELP! TOGETHER WE CAN MASTER THE TRIBE! SEE? *THEY* WILL HELP! YOUR WORDS ARE *POWER!* SPEAK YOUR WILL!

OHHHHHHHHN EIHHHHHHHN!

I? I HAVE THE POWER, ANCIENT ONE? THEN, I WISH TO BECOME *KING OF THE SWINE!* I WISH TO DO THEM *EVIL!!!* OHOOO- HOW COLD IT IS IN HERE...

HEAR HIM, *BLACK AVENGERS!* HE COMMANDS, AND YOU MUST OBEY THE MARKED ONE! *PLAGUE* THE VILLAGERS!! GO AND SPREAD *DEATH!!*

SEVERAL DAYS WENT BY WHILE MABU HID IN THE CAVE. DURING THE NIGHTS, THE WIND WHINED LIKE A STRICKEN ANIMAL, AND THE JUNGLE WHISPERED OF A STRANGE, STALKING DEATH! THEN...

LOOK, OLD ONE- THERE IS GREAT MISERY HERE!

YES- IT IS THE PLAGUE! THEY *FEAR* YOU NOW, MABU. I HAVE NOT SEEN SO MANY STRICKEN SINCE BEFORE YOU WERE BORN.! THE *FIENDS* PROTECT YOU, AND ASSAIL YOUR ENEMIES!

IT IS YOU, MABU- YOU AND THE ANCIENT ONE- THAT HAVE BROUGHT THIS *CURSE* ON OUR HEADS! MAY THE GODS STRIKE YOU DOWN!

SHOW HIM YOUR POWER, MABU!

FIENDS THAT ARE MY PROTECTORS- *HEAR ME! STOP* THE WORDS IN HIS THROAT!

AHHH-GG!! IT IS THE PLAGUE- THE PL...ARRRGG!!

ACKNOWLEDGE ME YOUR NEW KING AND I WILL *LIFT* THIS MISERY FROM YOU! OTHERWISE, YOU WILL ALL *DIE!*

SAVE US, MIGHTY ONE—FRIEND OF THE *BLACK SPIRITS...*

KING, KING! MAKE HIM OUR *KING!*

HELP US...HELP US...

ANY...ANYTHING YOU SAY, GREAT ONE! BUT SAVE MY CHILD...

SO MABU LIFTED THE CURSE ON THE PEOPLE AND HE BECAME THE CHIEFTAIN. ALL FEARED HIM AND OBEYED HIS EVERY COMMAND, UNTIL...

ANCIENT ONE, I AM *ILL*...THE PLAGUE HAS INFECTED ME, TOO. THE WHOLE WORLD SPINS...OHOOOO...

NO...NO, MABU—GREAT POWERS ARE *YOURS!* YOU *MUST* LIVE!

WELL, ANCIENT ONE? IS IT TRUE? IS MABU DEAD?

HE DOES NOT BREATHE—HIS HEART IS STILL. YES, HE HAS *DIED!* HIS POWER WAS TOO GREAT. IT HAS *CRACKED* HIS HEART!

THIS IS A *JOYOUS* DAY! THE TYRANT IS DEAD! QUICK, LET US BURY HIM AND FORGET HIS EVIL!

OH, THEY COULDN'T WAIT TO POUR THE EARTH ON MABU. THERE WAS NO SADNESS IN THE HEARTS OF THE MEN WHO CARRIED THE CASKET TO THE BURYING GROUNDS—AND NO WOMAN WEPT FOR HIS PASSING! BUT, THEN...

SOMETHING MOVES INSIDE!

OHOOOOO OHOOOOOO

BUMP! BUMP, BUMP! BUMP, BUMP.

LISTEN, DO YOU HEAR SOMETHING?

IT IS THE WIND IN THE TREE TOPS!

THERE IS NO WIND TO-NIGHT!

THE MEN FLED FROM THE CASKET, AND THEN, WITH A CREAK LIKE THE SPLITTING OF MEN'S BONES, THE TOP OF THE DEAD MABU'S CASKET BEGAN TO RISE! IN MY HUNDRED YEARS, I HAD NEVER SEEN SUCH AN EVIL THING...

LOOK, MABU *RISES!*

BUT THE *MARK* OF *DEATH* IS UPON HIM... HE LOOKS SO WHITE!

EEEEEEEEEEEEE!

MABU! I HAVE NEVER SEEN SUCH A THING AS *THIS!* I AM YOUR *SLAVE!*

THE *EDGE* OF *DEATH* IS *VERY DARK!* I HAVE BEEN WITH THE *FIENDS*—AND GREAT MISERY AND TORTURE AWAITS ME AFTER *I AM DEAD!* ANCIENT ONE, I MUST FIND A WAY TO LIVE *FOREVER!*

"ANCIENT ONE, YOU MUST FIND OUT HOW I AM TO DIE! IF I KNOW *THAT*, I WILL BE ABLE TO AVOID IT!"

"MABU! I HAVE ONLY CALLED ON THE SUPREME PRINCE OF EVIL ONCE BEFORE. BUT I WILL DO IT FOR *YOU*. I AM ONE OF HIS *DISCIPLES*—BUT I WARN YOU, HE WILL SEEK PAYMENT FOR REVEALING SECRETS BEYOND OUR UNDERSTANDING! I KEEP THE RITUAL RECORDED IN THE SKULL!"

"I HAVE SAID THE ANCIENT WORDS! RISE, OH PRINCE OF FIRE...THERE! THERE, MABU... HE HAS COME..."

"HE RISES OUT OF THE FLAMES!!"

I KNOW WHAT YOU SEEK OF ME, MABU... BUT FOR WHAT YOU SEEK YOU MUST SACRIFICE TO ME THE LIFE OF LOBLA~~~

THE FIGURE OF SMOKE THINNED AWAY, AND IN MABU'S EYES WAS THE LOOK OF MANIACAL JOY! HE LAUGHED WILDLY AND RUSHED OUT INTO THE NIGHT...

"*SEIZE HER*—QUICKLY! AND FOLLOW ME!"

"AS YOU WISH, *GREAT ONE!*"

"LET ME GO—LET ME GO! *HELP! HELP!*"

"THROW HER IN!"

"WE OBEY, MASTER!"

"NO, MABU...*NO!* AIEEEEEEEEEE!"

"I HAVE DONE AS YOU WISHED! NOW YOU MUST TELL ME..."

"MABUUUUU...A SILVER SPEAR FROM THE SKY WILL LEAD YOU TO THE DOOR OF DEATH...A SILVER SPEAR FROM THE SKY, MABUUUU..."

"HEE—HEE HEEEEEEEEE!!"

HARDLY HAD THE WORDS OF THE SPECTRE FADED INTO A HOLLOW ECHO, WHEN MABU SENT OUT A PROCLAMATION ON THE DRUMS THAT ALL THE NATIVES ON THE ISLAND MUST BRING HIM THEIR SILVER SPEARS OR FACE HORRIBLE TORTURE AND DEATH!..

"THAT'S IT!...THROW THEM OUT THERE! WHEN I HAVE EVERY SILVER SPEAR, THEN I AM *SAFE* FROM *DEATH!*"

"HEE-HEE! NO ONE OUT-WITS *DEATH* IN THE END—IT IS *KING!*"

WHY DID YOU DISOBEY MY ORDERS? YOU KNOW I ORDERED *EVERY* SILVER SPEAR SENT TO ME! SPEAK QUICKLY!

HEAR ME, GREAT MABU. THE SILVER SPEAR HAS BEEN IN MY FAMILY FOR GENERATIONS — HANDED DOWN AS A SACRED TRUST FROM FATHER TO SON. I WOULD DO YOU NO HARM WITH IT!!

YOU MUST LEARN TO OBEY — AND NOW YOU MUST PAY FOR LYING. YOU WERE GOING TO KILL ME WITH THAT SILVER SPEAR! I *KNOW*...

NO, MABU... I SWEAR... NO... *NO!!* AHHHHH!!

LISTEN TO THE SKY *ROAR*, ANCIENT ONE! BUT I FEAR NOTHING... NOTHING IN *THIS* WORLD!! NOT ONE SILVER SPEAR EXISTS ON THE ISLAND — AND I HAVE *FORBIDDEN* THE MAKING OF ANOTHER!!

WE SHALL SEE, MABU... HEE... HEE...

*B*UT AS MABU GLOATED INTO THE DARK, STORMY SKY, THINKING THAT HE WAS NOW SECURE FROM DEATH, THERE WAS SUDDENLY A CRASH AS IF TWO MOUNTAINS HAD COLLIDED, AND...

CRACK!

OHOOOOOO!!

NO! DON'T DO IT! YOU ARE BURYING HIM *ALIVE!* HE IS NOT DEAD — THE LIGHTNING ONLY *STUNNED* HIM!

WE DO NOT CARE, OLD ONE! THE SILVER SPEAR FROM THE SKY WAS THE VENGEANCE FROM THE GODS — AND NOW WE MUST ACT!

KEEP HER QUIET OR SHE WILL JOIN MABU!

*F*INALLY, THE ROCK WAS IN PLACE AND QUICKLY, SWIFTLY, THE MEN LEFT THAT PLACE, LEAVING AN OLD WOMAN TO WATCH AND HEAR...

ANCIENT ONE!! HELP ME... ... I . I C-CAN'T B-BUDGE THE BOULDER! HELP ME — OHOOO, THE *FIENDS!!* *THEY COME!!* THEY COME TO CLAIM ME! NO... NO... KEEP AWAY... KEEP AWA... AHHHHHH!!

THE PROPHECY WAS RIGHT! I CANNOT HELP YOU NOW, MABU. THE SILVER SPEAR FROM THE SKY HAS BROUGHT YOU TO THE DOOR OF DEATH AS IT WAS FORETOLD!! AND THE DOOR OF DEATH IS TOO HEAVY FOR MORTAL MAN TO MOVE! GOODBYE, MABU! HEE-HEE-HEEEE!

THE END

TERROR IN THE HEAVENS!

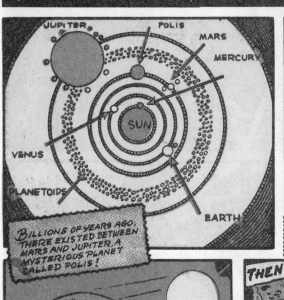

BILLIONS OF YEARS AGO, THERE EXISTED BETWEEN MARS AND JUPITER, A MYSTERIOUS PLANET CALLED POLIS!

LIFE ON THAT PLANET, CURIOUSLY ENOUGH, RESEMBLED THE EARLY LIFE ON EARTH. IT IS UNKNOWN WHETHER OR NOT HUMAN BEINGS, SUCH AS WE, EXISTED SOMEWHERE IN THE TANGLED VEGETATION OF POLIS.

POLIS HOWEVER WAS TOO CLOSE TO JUPITER. GRADUALLY IT WAS DRAWN TO THE GIANT PLANET BY THE TREMENDOUS GRAVITATIONAL PULL OF JUPITER....

THEN...

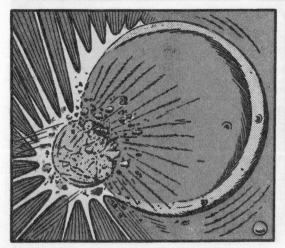

IF YOU WERE TO LOOK UP AT THE HEAVENS THROUGH A TELESCOPE, YOU WOULD SEE THE REMAINS OF THE PLANET POLIS AS MOONS REVOLVING AROUND MARS AND JUPITER.

THE GHOST OF THE RUE DE MORTE

So you don't believe in ghosts? Well, neither do a lot of other people. Paul Reynard was a non-believer... until he met...

THE TIME: EARLY 1900'S. THE PLACE: THE SLUMS OF PARIS...

MON DIEU! THOSE LITTLE CROOKS WILL BE THE DEATH OF ME YET. THEY ARE WORSE THAN LES BOCHES!

COME ON! COME ON! HE IS AFTER US!

HE IS FAT AND SLOW... THERE IS NO NEED TO RUN FAST!

WHEW-- I AGREE. LET'S STOP FOR AWHILE.

EIGHT O'CLOCK, KNOW WHAT THAT MEANS?

TIME FOR THE GHOST WHICH HAS ALL OF PARIS FRIGHTENED!

I DON'T BELIEVE THERE IS ANY GHOST. BUT SINCE THERE IS NOTHING BETTER TO DO, LET'S GO TO THE RUE DE MORTE AND I WILL SHOW YOU THE GHOST IS A FAKE!

STEALING THROUGH THE POLICE LINES WHICH SURROUND THE STRANGE RUE DE MORTE, THE BOYS WAIT FOR THE GHOST.

MY PAPA SAYS TO STAY AWAY FROM THE ALLEY WHEN THE CLOCK STRIKES EIGHT. IT IS NOT WISE TO TAMPER WITH THE UNNATURAL, HE SAYS.

BAH, YOUR PAPA IS A FOOL IF HE BELIEVES THAT THE GHOST REALLY EXISTS!

THEN HOW COME THE POLICE ARE HERE? IF YOU'RE SO SMART, PAUL, ANSWER THAT!

THEY'RE HERE TO STOP PEOPLE LIKE YOU FROM GETTING FRIGHTENED. IF IT WERE REALLY TRUE, WHERE IS YOUR GHOST? IT'S EIGHT O'CLOCK ALREADY!

THE GHOST SHOULD BE HERE ANY SECOND!

QUIET YOU TWO... AND WATCH THAT DOOR!

THERE HE IS! THERE HE IS!

BAH, I TELL YOU THAT IS NO GHOST, BUT MERELY AN OLD DRUNK WHO LIVES IN THAT HOUSE! COME, THROW THINGS AT HIM AND THEN WE'LL SEE IF HE'S REALLY A GHOST!

JUST AS THE LEGEND SAYS! EVERY NIGHT WHEN THE CLOCK IN THE SQUARE STRIKES EIGHT, THE GHOST SHALL APPEAR AND WALK THE RUE DE MORTE!

THERE, DID YOU SEE THAT ONE HIT!

NONSENSE, YOU DIDN'T EVEN COME CLOSE TO HIM!

BUT I HIT HIM, TOO! THEY GO RIGHT THROUGH HIM THOUGH!

...AND I SAY HE IS A GHOST... THOSE STONES WENT RIGHT THROUGH HIM!

AND I SAY THERE IS NO SUCH A THING AS A GHOST! IF HE IS A GHOST, WHY DOES HE DO NOTHING BUT WALK UP AND DOWN THIS ALLEY?

WELL, I DON'T KNOW WHO'S RIGHT, BUT LOOK...!

HE'S GONE...AND THERE'S NOTHING UP THERE BUT A DEAD END!

AND IF HE ISN'T A GHOST, HOW DID HE GET THROUGH THE WALL?

PROBABLY STEPPED INTO ONE OF THE DOORWAYS ALONG THE ALLEY, THAT'S HOW! BUT I SEE THERE'S NO CONVINCING YOU TWO--SO LET'S GO BACK TO MONSIEUR LA FROID'S. I'M GETTING HUNGRY!

The years passed quickly, and as is the way with most childhood friendships, the trio split up and went their separate ways. Realizing that his chances for success were limited in the slums, Paul Reynard turned to the other parts of the city to seek his fortune. Fate was good to Paul, and it wasn't long before the ruffian from the slums had been changed into a successful young business man...

BUT, LIKE EVERY MAN, PAUL OCCASIONALLY RETURNED TO THE SCENE OF HIS CHILDHOOD.

...AND HERE'S WHERE WE USED TO STEAL COOKIES FROM MONSIEUR LA FROID! AH, THOSE WERE THE GOOD OLD DAYS...

ALMOST EIGHT O'CLOCK! HMMM... ABOUT TIME FOR THE GHOST OF RUE DE MORTE TO MAKE HIS ENTRANCE. NEVER DID FIND OUT IF THAT STORY WAS TRUE... BUT THERE'S NO TIME LIKE THE PRESENT TO FIND OUT!

PLACE HASN'T CHANGED MUCH... A LITTLE DIRTIER THAN BEFORE, BUT THAT'S ALL. THERE'S THAT DOORWAY... WELL, I'LL STICK AROUND 'TIL EIGHT AND SEE WHAT HAPPENS!

BUT, AT THAT INSTANT...

WHAT THE...!

GET HIM, JEAN... HE LOOKS LIKE HE'S CARRYING PLENTY OF FRANCS.

AND HE SHOULD BE GLAD TO SHARE THEM ...AFTER I CONVINCE HIM!

IT IS JUST AS I SAID... THIS WALLET IS FULL!

JEAN! PHILLIPE! MY TWO OLD FRIENDS!

LOOK! HE'S PAUL REYNARD! AND HE HAS RECOGNIZED US! THAT MEANS HE WILL PROBABLY REPORT US TO THE GENDARMES! THERE IS ONLY ONE WAY TO MAKE SURE HE DOESN'T...LIKE THIS...!

THERE! THAT TAKES CARE OF HIM... HE WON'T REPORT US TO ANYONE NOW!

JEAN! JEAN! OHHHH... NOoo-oo!

HURRY, JEAN... LET'S GET OUT OF HERE BEFORE SOMEONE SEES US!

HOW DEATH VALLEY GOT ITS NAME

DEATH VALLEY IS 130 MILES LONG WITH HALF OF IT BELOW SEA LEVEL AND IS COLORED IN SPOTS LIKE A DEADLY CORAL SNAKE. THE INDIANS CALL THE GREAT PIT, *TOMESHA*, MEANING GROUND FIRE.

ON CHRISTMAS 1849, A MORMON PARTY, KNOWN AS THE JAYHAWKERS PUSHED TOWARD TOMESHA ON THEIR WAY TO CALIFORNIA. LITTLE DID THESE PIONEERS KNOW OF THE DANGERS THAT LAY AHEAD.

ALMOST IMMEDIATELY, THEY HIT IMPASSABLE GROUNDS. WAGONS HAD TO BE DRAGGED OVER JAGGED BOULDERS. AND, IF THAT WASN'T ENOUGH, THE WATER AND FOOD SUPPLIES BEGAN TO RUN LOW.

WAGONS WERE TOO CLUMSY FOR TOMESHA. SO THE JAYHAWKERS BURNED THEIR WAGONS TO ROAST THE MEAT OF DYING OXEN, AND LOADED THEIR BELONGINGS ON THE REMAINING OXEN.

MORE THAN HALF OF THE JAYHAWKERS STRAYED AND DIED OF STARVATION.

FORTY DAYS LATER... LIKE THE 40 YEARS OF THE ISRAELITES... THE PITIFUL SURVIVORS REACHED SAN FERNANDO MISSION, WITH A NAME FOR TOMESHA. SINCE THEN, IT HAS BEEN KNOWN AS DEATH VALLEY.

GOODBYE, DEATH VALLEY!

WEIRD WORLDS

As on earth, the various societies on other planets have their problems with crime and punishment, too. Some of the different penalties imposed by peoples of other worlds are pictured below.

On the side of Mercury where there is always night, the criminal is strapped to a rock and his body smeared with a certain juice. This juice attracts the Horaks, the man-eating ants of MERCURY! As the ants approach him, the criminal can see their bobbing lighted antennas. Then the light from the antennas becomes blinding and he feels thousands of jaws tearing at his unprotected skin.

Uranus has devised what is probably one of the most horrible punishments found anywhere. The offender is placed across the top of a mound, a heavy rock suspended from his hands down one side of the mound and another heavy boulder suspended from his feet down the other side of the mound. The boulders are kept from rolling down the mound by ice pegs which melt when the sun comes up. Then...

Named for the Greek god of the lower world, PLUTO has many tortures to sway a man from a life of crime. One of them is to run razor sharp knives over the body of the criminal and then throw him into a pool of heavily salted water!

In Neptune, the condemned one is forced to hang over a pit of snarling Shapir by holding onto a hollow pipe which runs over the pit. As the minutes pass, warm, then steaming hot water is pumped through the pipe. The man lives as long as he can grasp the burning metal.

CHAMBER OF
HILLS
TALES OF TERROR AND SUSPENSE
CHAMBER OF
CHILLS
PDC
10¢
lo.22
AUG.
MAGAZINE
WHAT HAVE YOU DONE TO ME? WHERE IS MY SISTER?
VE
ARE
OU....
..TO
EN THE
STERIOUS
OOR INTO
WORLD
OF
ORROR!
COSMOS AGING MACHINE

WELCOME!

Friends... the night is dark and the wind is cold! Don't shiver out there. At least in here you'll be warm... perspiring, in fact! You say we have no stove? No! We only have bloodcurdling horror and mind-defying mystery... both so calculated as to make you boil with FEAR!

But before we start our journey into the realms of high adventure and throbbing terror, let us read some of the letters you wrote us about the last issue of CHAMBER OF CHILLS!

SUSPENSE!!!

Once I picked up an issue of CHAMBER OF CHILLS, I just couldn't put it down. The suspense was terrific!

F. D., Boston, Mass.

DARN GOOD!!!

All of your stories were really spine-tingling. I don't know how you do it but they're darn good!

B. M., Wilmington, Calif.

WEIRD!!!

Your book has hit the top of my list for weird and mysterious tales.

C. L., Seattle, Wash.

SOMETHING GREAT!!!

I enjoy reading your CHAMBER OF CHILLS more than any other book. It has that something which makes it great!

P. J., Detroit, Mich.

AND NOW... TURN THE PAGE AND BEGIN THIS ISSUE OF

CHAMBER OF CHILLS

CHAMBER OF CHILLS MAGAZINE, AUGUST, 1951, Vol. 1, No. 22, IS PUBLISHED EVERY OTHER MONTH by WITCHES TALES, INC., 1860 Broadway, New York 23, N.Y. Application for second class entry pending at the Post Office at New York, N.Y. under the Act of March 3, 1879. Single copies 10c. Subscription rates, 10 issues for $1.00 in the U.S. and possessions, elsewhere $1.50. All names in this periodical are entirely fictitious and no identification with actual persons is intended. Contents copyrighted, 1951, by Witches Tales, Inc., New York City.

Printed in the U.S.A.

THE VAULT of LIVING DEATH!

The RESTLESS, TORMENTED DEAD DO NOT LIE STILL, BUT RAVE AND SCREAM IN DEATH'S GARDEN... AND THERE'S A SECRET, LOCKED IN THE MOLDY COFFINS THAT CAUSES DEAD MEN TO WALK AGAIN IN...

THIS MONEY IS TO BE USED FOR THE UPKEEP OF MY LATE FRIEND'S GRAVE. OCCASIONAL FLOWERS... GOOD LORD!! IT...IT'S *HIM!!*

WHAT'S THE MATTER, DOCTOR? IS SOMETHING WRONG?

DUE TO A CERTAIN TOWN'S COMMERCIAL GROWTH, IT BECAME NECESSARY TO MOVE A CEMETERY TO THE OUTSKIRTS OF THE TOWN. THIS *UNEARTHING* OF THE *DEAD* WAS INTRUSTED TO TWO AGED *GRAVE-DIGGERS*, NEAR *CORPSES* THEMSELVES, WHO MOVED SOFTLY FROM STONE TO STONE AFTER SUNSET...

IT'S BEST WE DIG *AFTER DARK,* FRIEND AMOS! SEEIN' THE *DEAD* WOULD DISTURB MOST OF THE *LIVIN'!*

AY, JONATHAN! PRYING INTO THE PRIVACY OF THE HALLOWED *DEAD* IS NOT VERY PRETTY...

'TIS AN EASY TASK THOUGH, AMOS. NO TROUBLE FINDIN' THESE PEOPLE AT HOME! *HEH HEH!*

SOMETIMES THE COFFINS SINK A FOOT OR TWO! I'D HATE TO LOOK *INSIDE* A BOX!

AFTER EACH *NOCTURNAL VISIT*, MORE *EMPTY GRAVES YAWN CRUELLY*, LIKE *GIANT SHARKS ROBBED* OF THEIR *PREY*...

SLOW BUT SURE, THAT'S THE WAY TO BE WHEN YE DIG UP A CEMETERY...

LOOK! THERE'S OLD DOC MATLOCK'S VAULT... BUSIEST MAN I EVER KNOWED! BET HE'S SITTIN' THERE RIGHT NOW DOIN' SOME EXPERIMENTS! HEH! HEH!

THE DOOR OF THE *FETID TOMB*, UNAIRED, UNLIT FOR FORTY YEARS, IS FORCED OPEN, AND THE AIR, WITH A GUSH LIKE THE *SIGH* OF A *LOST DEMON*, RUSHES IN...

J-JONATHAN!! L-*LOOK!* THE *COFFIN*, IT...IT'S *EMPTY!!*

IT MUST HAVE BEEN THE *DEVIL*, HIMSELF, WHO CLAIMED THE *FLESHLESS REMAINS*...

THE *DAMP* BREEZE ECHOED *HOLLOWLY, MOURNFULLY* AGAINST THE *MOIST GREY* WALLS OF THE *DANK* MAUSOLEUM...THEN, BARELY AUDIBLE, THE CRISP RUSTLE OF...

PAPERS! A MESSAGE! CLOSE THE DOOR, THE WIND'S BLOWING THEM!

TO GET A *STRANGE CHILL* IN MY BONES, AND MY FLESH FEELS AS IF *SPIDERS* WERE *CRAWLING* ALL OVER IT!!

EEEYAHH!! IT'S --IT'S *MATLOCK!* HE...HE WAS *TRYING TO GET OUT!!*

OH, GOD! *HE MUST HAVE BEEN*... I...I CAN'T *THINK* OF IT!!!

I'M BEGINNING

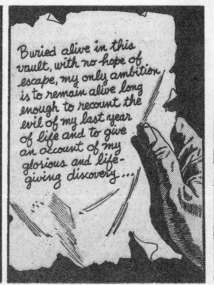

WHAT TALE OF HORROR HAD THE MAN WHO SOUGHT TO ESCAPE HIS TOMB TO TELL? IN THE FLICKERING, WEIRD, LAMP-LIGHT THE HUNTERS OF CORPSES BENT OVER THE ANCIENT, YELLOW PAGES... SLOWLY, THEIR MINDS TRANSCENDED FOUR DECADES...

Buried alive in this vault, with no hope of escape, my only ambition is to remain alive long enough to recount the evil of my last year of life and to give an account of my glorious and life-giving discovery...

IT *WORKS! WE* HAVE *SUCCEEDED!* NOW SURGERY CAN BE PERFORMED WITHOUT FEAR OF *SHOCK!* WE HAVE GIVEN THE WORLD ITS FIRST SUCCESSFUL *ANESTHETIC!*

WHAT DO YOU MEAN *"WE"*? IT WAS *MY DISCOVERY!* YOU WERE *MERELY* MY ASSISTANT. *I* SHALL TAKE THE CREDIT!

NO! I SHALL *SHARE* THE *HONORS!* I HAVE SPENT TEN YEARS OF MY LIFE, EXPERIMENTING AND DOING RESEARCH, TO PROVE AND TO BRING TO LIFE AN IDEA YOU HAD. HOWEVER, THE MOST IMPORTANT THING NOW IS TO TEST THE DISCOVERY ON A HUMAN BEING!

YOU'RE RIGHT! THE IMPORTANT THING IS THE DISCOVERY!

AND *YOU* SHALL BE THE GUINEA PIG! *THEN* WE'LL SEE WHO GETS THE ACCLAIM!

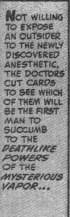

NOT WILLING TO EXPOSE AN OUTSIDER TO THE NEWLY DISCOVERED ANESTHETIC, THE DOCTORS CUT CARDS TO SEE WHICH OF THEM WILL BE THE FIRST MAN TO SUCCUMB TO THE *DEATHLIKE POWERS* OF THE *MYSTERIOUS VAPOR...*

I HAVE THE KING! CAN YOU TOP IT!

I'M AFRAID NOT! ARE YOU STILL WILLING TO BE EXPERIMENTED ON? I WISH IT HAD BEEN ME!

HA! HA! THE CARDS WERE *STACKED* AGAINST YOU FROM THE BEGINNING, DR. RUSSELL!

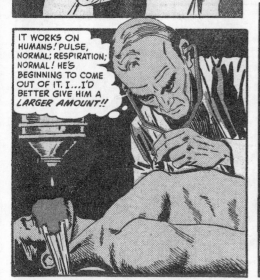

IT WORKS ON HUMANS! PULSE, NORMAL; RESPIRATION; NORMAL! HE'S BEGINNING TO COME OUT OF IT. I...I'D BETTER GIVE HIM A *LARGER AMOUNT!!*

WHAT THOUGHTS *CRAWLED* THROUGH THE *EVIL MIND* OF DR. MATLOCK AND CAUSED THE *GHASTLY SMILE* TO PLAY ABOUT HIS LIPS? ELATION? PARTIALLY, BUT IT WAS ALSO SOMETHING *MORE SINISTER, MORE HORRID* THAN EVEN THE WET, RED LIPS OF A VAMPIRE...

...AND SO, GENTLEMEN, I PRONOUNCE MY *BELOVED* COLLEAGUE, DR. RUSSELL, *DEAD* OF A RARE, UNKNOWN DISEASE, WHICH HE CONTRACTED WHILE WORKING WITH THESE ANIMALS! I AM HEARTBROKEN, OF COURSE! THE WORLD HAS LOST A GREAT SCIENTIST!

IMPATIENT TILL THE MOIST BROWN EARTH SHOULD *SEAL* THOSE LIPS FOREVER, MATLOCK'S BREAST BEAT LIKE THE MUFFLED OARS OF THE FERRY TO THE INFERNAL REGIONS...

SOB-- SOB-- SOB!!

I HOPE I GAVE HIM ENOUGH OF THE STUFF! I WISH TO SATAN THEY'D HURRY! *WHAT'S THAT!!* DID THE COFFIN *MOVE?* NO, IT'S JUST MY NERVES!!

DR. MATLOCK'S VISIBLY AFFECTED BY HIS FRIEND'S DEATH, ISN'T HE?

IN HIS STUDY, DR. MATLOCK'S ELATION IS DIMMED BY FEAR AND CONSCIENCE...

WHY COULDN'T THE FOOL SEE IT *MY WAY?* CAN HE POSSIBLY GET OUT? NO, HE WOULD SUFFOCATE THREE MINUTES AFTER THE EARTH COVERED HIM! BUT WHY WORRY? MY NAME ALONE SHALL BE THE GREATEST IN THE MEDICAL PROFESSION! EH? WHAT WAS THAT?

AIEEEEEE!! NO! NO! IT CAN'T BE! DON'T COME NEAR ME!

AT THE SIGHT OF THE *ROTTED, FESTERED FACE*, MATLOCK'S MIND FELL INTO THE *BLACK, BOTTOMLESS* PIT OF UNCONSCIOUSNESS, WHERE HE WAS VISITED BY THE *FORMLESS, WRITHING FIENDS* OF *HELL*, WHO CRIED...

DR. MATLOCK! DR. MATLOCK! WHAT'S HAPPENED? OH, YOU POOR MAN! THE FUNERAL WAS TOO MUCH FOR YOU!

OH, MRS. DOLAN! I MUST HAVE FALLEN ASLEEP AT MY DESK. I HAD A TERRIBLE NIGHTMARE!

IT'S MY NERVES! I SHOULD GET SOME SLEEP. *NO!!* I *CAN'T* SLEEP... I MIGHT *TALK!*

A FEAR OF *SLEEP*, MINGLED WITH THE *GHASTLY APPARITION*, LEFT THE DOCTOR *HALF CRAZED* WITH DOUBT AND DISBELIEF...

MAYBE IT WAS..?? BUT...BUT I HELPED *BURY* HIM! WAIT! I HAVE TO FIND OUT! I'LL *DIG HIM UP...* I MUST KNOW!

DRAWN BY A POWER, A *FORCE* WHICH WAS NOT A CONSCIOUS PART OF HIM, DR. MATLOCK MADE HIS WAY TO THE *GRAVEYARD*, AND LIKE A *GHOUL* IN QUEST OF A SUCCULENT, *ROTTING CORPSE*, HE DUG FEVERISHLY...

HE'S *GONE!* NOT EVEN A TRACE OF THE *COFFIN!!* WHAT SHALL I DO? WHERE CAN I HIDE?? I... MUST...GET... OUT...OF... HERE!

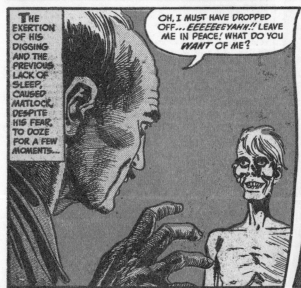

THE EXERTION OF HIS DIGGING AND THE PREVIOUS LACK OF SLEEP, CAUSED MATLOCK, DESPITE HIS FEAR, TO DOZE FOR A FEW MOMENTS...

OH, I MUST HAVE DROPPED OFF...*EEEEEEEYAHH!!* LEAVE ME IN PEACE! WHAT DO YOU *WANT* OF ME?

MATLOCK IS UNABLE TO SLEEP, UNWILLING TO CONSORT WITH OTHER MEN FOR FEAR OF GIVING HIMSELF AWAY. HIS BODY AND FEATURES BEGIN TO *TWIST* LIKE THE *GNARLED FINGERS* OF A *LEPROUS WITCH*...

PERHAPS I'LL FEEL BETTER AFTER I SHAVE!... MAYBE THE NIGHTMARES WILL... *AAAAAAHH!!* HELP! HELP!!

NOW THE *GHASTLY VISAGE* OF RUSSELL HAUNTS HIM AT EVERY TURN... HE FEARS EVERY FOOTSTEP BEHIND HIM, AND HE CRINGES BEFORE EVERY HUMAN FORM AS A *SLIMY TOAD* BEFORE THE *DRIPPING FANGS* OF A *VIPER*...

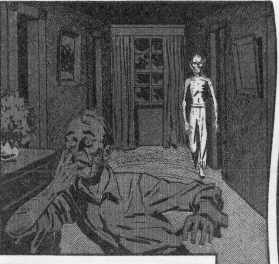

LACK OF FOOD AND REST TOOK ITS TOLL AND LEFT HIM HAGGARD AND RESTLESS AS A BIRD OF CARRION IN A LAND WHERE NO ONE DIES...

SLEEP... *SLEEP!* I MUST GET SOME SLEEP...THE ANESTHETIC....YES! WHY DIDN'T I THINK OF IT BEFORE!

DESPERATE, HE ALLOWS THE *DROPS OF FORGETFULNESS* TO ENVELOPE HIS *WEARY BRAIN*...SLOWLY... SLOWLY, THE *DARKNESS*, LIKE *DEATH*, CLOSES IN...

AH! AT *LAST!* RUSSELL-- YOU--CAN'T--HURT--ME-- NOW!!

WORRIED ABOUT THE DOCTOR THE TOWN DIGNITARIES SEEK HIM OUT AND...

I'D SAY OFF-HAND, THOUGH I'M NOT A DOCTOR, THAT THE SYMPTOMS ARE THE SAME AS DR. RUSSELL'S! PROBABLY GOT IT FROM THE SAME ANIMALS!

WE HAD BETTER *BURY* HIM AND AVOID THE POSSIBILITY OF THIS SICKNESS SPREADING!

JUST THINK! HE DIED TRYING TO MAKE THE WORLD A BETTER PLACE FOR US!

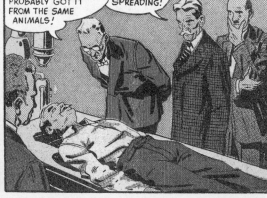

SLOWLY, THE BEREAVED FEET OF THE TOWNS-PEOPLE CARRY THE SLEEPING DR. MATLOCK TO HIS FINAL RESTING PLACE, TO THE *CRAWLING TOMB* WHERE ETERNITY IS LIKE THE TICKING OF A CLOCK... SLOW... SURE...

HE'D BE PROUD TO KNOW THAT THE PEOPLE HE SERVED BOUGHT HIM THIS VAULT!

SOB... SOB...

IT'S THE LEAST WE COULD DO!

AFTER THE SHORT RITUAL THE DOORS WERE RELUCTANTLY *CLOSED* AND *SEALED FOREVER!* THEN, SUDDENLY *SOMETHING STIRRED* WITHIN THE CASKET...

CREEEAK!

WHERE...WHERE AM I? THIS ROOM...IT LOOKS VAGUELY FAMILIAR...A *COFFIN!* OH, NO, THEY *COULDN'T!!* I--I'M STILL DREAMING!!

LITTLE BY LITTLE, THE SITUATION TOOK ON MEANING! GRADUALLY, IT HIT HIM WITH THE IMPACT OF A POISONOUS FLUID RUNNING THRU HIS VEINS AND WHEN THE PUTRID VENOM HIT HIS BRAIN...

HELP!! HELP!! LET ME OUT!! DON'T LEAVE ME!! SOB--SOB--SOB!

MADLY, SAVAGELY, HE THROWS HIS WEIGHT AGAINST THE SOLID DOOR, UNTIL HIS BONES ARE ALL BUT *CRUSHED.* THE DOOR DOESN'T GIVE AN INCH, AND HIS CRIES AND PLEAS ECHO AND RE-ECHO HOLLOWLY IN THE DRIPPING, CHILLING VAULT...

HELP! HELP!! SOB--SOB. LET ME OUT!! SOB-- SOB!

HELP! HELP! OUT! OUT. SOB!!

THUMP!

I...MUST... GET...OUT!

THE WILL TO LIVE PERSISTS, BUT THERE IS NO LONGER THE STRENGTH. WITHOUT FOOD AND WATER, MIND AND BODY WOULD NOT COORDINATE...

MY BODY *CRIES* FOR FOOD... MY SKIN GROWS THIN...

WHAT SUSTENANCE HE COULD FIND CAME FROM THE *OOZING WALLS* OF *DEATH* ITSELF...

WATER! A LITTLE WATER!

SURROUNDED BY DEATH, THERE IS A FINAL RESIGNATION. THE CREEPING DOOM, LIKE A COLONY OF CANNIBAL ANTS, COMES TO REMOVE THE OUTER LAYER OF FLESH, LEAVING ONLY BONES, INSENSITIVE TO PAIN AND SHOCK...

IT'S *NO USE*...CAN'T GET OUT...MUST GET THINGS IN ORDER...

LET ME SEE...FULL CONFESSION... FORMULA FOR ANESTHETIC... NO ONE'LL EVER FIND IT ANYWAY, BUT I HAVE TO LEAVE IT BEHIND ME...

WELL, THAT'S FINISHED... ONLY ONE MORE THING LEFT TO DO - *DIE!*

THEN THE HEART, WHICH HAD BEEN FILLED WITH *HATE* AND *AMBITION* AND THEN *GRIPPED* WITH *FEAR,* FLUTTERED WEAKLY, GAINED MOMENTUM, THEN STOPPED; LIKE THE MUSIC OF A SAVAGE DANCE WHEN THE PRISONER IS ABOUT TO BE CONSUMED...

COUGH...COUGH ...AAAAH...

DEATH AND *TIME* ARE ALSO SAVAGES WHO *CONSUME THEIR VICTIMS...*

... AND IN THEIR OWN UNHURRIED WAY, *TEAR OFF THE FLESH*...

... AND PICK THE BONES CLEAN!!!

THE AMBER RAYS OF THE LANTERN REACHED OUT LIKE TENTACLES, DRAWING TOGETHER THE BRITTLE SCRAPS OF PAPER AND THE CRUMBLING HEAP OF BONES, WHICH ONCE ENACTED WHAT THE PAPERS DESCRIBED! THE GRAVE-DIGGERS RETURNED FROM THEIR INCREDIBLE VENTURE INTO THE PAST...

IT...IT'S UNBELIEVABLE! WHY, I USED TO SIT ON THAT...THAT KNEE, FRIEND AMOS, WHEN THERE WAS *FLESH* UPON IT...

MAYBE WE'D BETTER GET BACK TO OUR WORK AND LET THIS...THIS *NIGHTMARE* PASS!

HURRY UP, CAN'T YOU? I WANT TO GET OUT OF THIS *DRIPPING CELL*...

WAIT! GET THOSE PAPERS! THEN WE'LL FIND DOC RUSSELL'S GRAVE...

ON STONE AFTER STONE, THE AMBER LANTERN LICKED AWAY THE MOIST, BLACK DARKNESS...

NO! THIS IS NOT THE ONE, EITHER! IT MUST BE AROUND HERE SOMEWHERE!

HAVE WE LOOKED ON THE OTHER SIDE OF THE OAK TREE?

AY, WE SHOULD HAVE LOOKED NEAR THE *HAUNTED OAK* FIRST, FOR...

HERE IT IS!! BUT HOW DO WE KNOW HE'S *IN IT!!*

DAVID RUSSELL

THE END

PORTRAIT OF FEAR

"There's something evil about this place!" Ben Lawrence exclaimed. "Your uncle didn't know it when he was alive . . . he was always at sea. I took care of renting the place for him, and *I* know! All of the last three tenants — young gentlemen like yourself — were found dead in their beds! Dead of heart failure. . . .

"No one knows just what happened," the lawyer continued quietly. "They just dropped out of sight. And each time, when the constable came to this house to investigate, he found a pile of old newspapers and a row of milk bottles that had never been taken inside out on the steps, a load of yellow, mildewed letters that had never been taken out of the mail box, and inside this house . . . the young men, fully dressed and DEAD on the bed!"

"Well!" gasped Hal Carlyle, his eyes turning from the lawyer at his side to the gray stone house that loomed so large before them in the gathering dusk. "Well! Very nice of Uncle George to leave the place to me in his will! I guess the least I can do in return is to solve the mystery immediately!"

Nothing Ben Lawrence could say would dissuade his young client, so with troubled eyes and a heavy heart, the lawyer took his leave. Hal was left alone.

It was an ordinary-enough house, Hal decided finally, relaxing on his bed after a tour of inspection. Ben Lawrence was just an imaginative old . . .

He leaped violently to his feet. There was something . . . or someone . . . in the bedroom with him! There had been a sound of some kind . . . and a vague, pleasant odor . . . Suddenly, Hal knew! What he had heard was the unmistakable sound of a woman brushing her hair! And the odor was the scent of fine, French perfume!

"Who is it?" Hal called urgently. "Don't be afraid. I won't hurt you."

But his only answer was a barely-perceptible flickering of the electric lights and a low, almost inaudible laugh . . . the tinkling, silvery laugh of a beautiful woman! It was the laugh that did it! It was maddening! He ran from room to room with his heart pounding, determined to find the *thing* that was laughing at him! There was no sound at all now, not even the rustle of silk that he'd followed at first, but somehow Hal *knew* it was there . . . teasing him, leading him on, daring him to find it!

Finally, he gave up the chase, and sank back wearily on his bed again. "This is ridiculous! I know there wasn't anything," he thought to himself grimly.

The laugh tinkled again—as though his invisible companion was reading his mind! Hal looked up sharply, his eye caught by a bubble of pale, glittering light that suddenly illuminated a picture hanging on the opposite wall. His breath jammed in his throat! It was a portrait of a woman—tall and unbelievably beautiful, her smoke-color eyes smiling down at him, her rosy lips curved in a smile. Hal had never even dreamed of such beauty. He lay there gaping, dimly understanding that the bubble of light, the sounds he'd heard and the woman in the portrait were all one and the same!

"It is YOU, isn't it?" he whispered, his eyes never moving from the picture. The pale light danced up and down the wall. The room filled with the intoxicating scent of perfume. The rustle of silks and satins grew louder, and slowly, unbelievably, the lady of the portrait gathered her skirts together daintily, and stepped out of her frame, the light forming an unearthly halo around her head! She walked towards Hal noiselessly, her lips still curved in that same vacant smile, her eyes hard and penetrating, boring into his . . .

"NO! Please . . . don't . . ." Hal pleaded, terror striking at his heart. But the lady just smiled . . . bent her head gracefully and, with lips as cold and clammy as seaweed, kissed him.

* *

Ben Lawrence was scared. He hadn't heard a word from Hal Carlyle since the fateful day he'd left the boy alone in that accursed house! Walking up the driveway now, the lawyer tried to tell himself that he was being foolish, that Hal was perfectly all right . . .

Suddenly he gave a choked little cry, his face turning the color of pale, wet cement! On the doorstep lay a pile of old, uncollected newspapers! Beside them stood a row of milk bottles that had never been taken inside! In the mail box lay a number of yellow, mildewed letters! A faint odor of decay hung in the air. . . .

IN THE MYSTERIOUS HEART OF THE BLACK NIGHT LURK FOUL AND EVIL CREATURES FAWNED BY THE DEVIL AND NURSED BY WITCHES AND DEMONS! ONE MAN SOUGHT TO ENTER THEIR CULT OF ABANDON, TO LIVE IN UNHOLY ECSTASY BESIDE THE...

CREATURES OF THE SWAMP

MY FRIEND! FELLOW INITIATE IN *EVIL*! YOU ARE *MY* CREATION! MINE! *HEH! HEH! HEH!*

YOU MUST FREE ME FROM THIS *MONSTROUS* PLACE! I CAN'T *BEAR* IT ANY LONGER!

IN THE STUDIO OF THE MAYFORD ART SCHOOL, A *STRANGE* AND *TORMENTED* MIND GAZES WITH INTENSE RAPTURE ON THE PRODUCTS OF ITS CREATION... PICTURES FORMED OUT OF A WILD AND FEVERISH IMAGINATION...

LOOK AT GLOOMY OLD JULIAN ADMIRING HIS ART! HE NEVER USES ANY COLORS BUT *BLACK* AND *GREEN*!

HE FRIGHTENS ME! LOOK AT HIS *EYES*!

LAUGH, YOU *FOOLS*! YOU WILL NEVER KNOW THE POWER MY HANDS CAN BRING TO LIFE!

HOW ABOUT DINNER TONIGHT, DARLING?

FINE, GLEN! YOU CAN PICK ME UP AT EIGHT!

DINNER WITH *HIM*! *STUPID GIRL*! IF SHE KNEW OF THE DARK AND SECRET WORLDS I COULD UNLEASH FOR HER, AND HER *ALONE*!

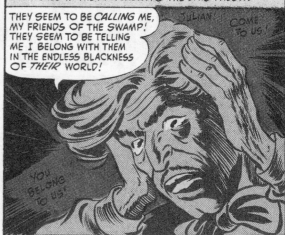

I MUST GET OUT OF HERE *AT ONCE!* THERE'S SOMETHING *STRANGE* AND *HORRIBLE* IN THE AIR -- I CAN FEEL IT!

SHE IS *FRIGHTENED* OF ME! I MUSTN'T LET HER LEAVE TO CARRY MY SECRET TO CURIOUS EARS! WHERE IS MY BOOK-- MY BOOK?

YOU DON'T BELIEVE THAT MY WORLD OF THE SWAMP *EXISTS*, DO YOU? I'LL *PROVE* IT TO YOU!! *YOU* WILL *JOIN* ME THERE, AND WE WILL LIVE IN ITS MURKY DEPTHS--*TOGETHER-FOREVER!* I'LL READ THIS INCANTATION!

NO! NO! HELP! AHH-H-H!

OH, CREATURES OF THE NIGHT, PERMIT ME TO ENTER INTO YOUR *FORBIDDEN REALM* WHERE *DARKNESS* AND *EVIL* REIGN FOREVER! OPEN YOUR DOORS TO ONE *DEVOTED* TO SERVE YOU AND WORSHIP YOU! *EXCRANTA, TAIBORAI DAMYATA!*

IN ONE *WILD* AND *SUDDEN* FLASH OF LIGHT, A SINISTER DREAM, FORMED IN A TWISTED MIND, BECOMES A REALITY...AND ALL *SPACE* AND *TIME* DISAPPEAR AS A STRANGE TRANSFORMATION TAKES PLACE!

AT LAST! MY CREATION COME TO LIFE IN ALL ITS *EVIL* AND *HORROR!* THIS IS THE DEVIL'S *OWN* LAIR AND I AM SWORN TO SERVE THE *PRINCE OF NIGHT!*

WHERE ARE WE? HELP! HELP!!

YOU MUSTN'T BE AFRAID, MARY! THIS IS ONE OF MY *BELOVED* FRIENDS TO WHOM I DEDICATE MY MIND AND SOUL!! AND SO MUST *YOU!!*

NEVER! NEVER! HOW HORRIBLE! I *MUST* BE DREAMING!

HIS EYES BURNING WITH THE VISION OF EVIL PREVIOUSLY *HIDDEN* FROM MAN, JULIAN WANDERS THROUGH THE INFESTED WORLD OF HIS IMAGINATION, NOW *REAL* AND *ALIVE*...AND *SHOCKING*...

OH, WORLD OF THE SWAMP, YOU CALLED AND I *CAME* TO YOU, KNOWING THERE WOULD BE *NO RETURN!!* PROTECT US FROM THE WORLD OF LIGHT AND WRAP US IN THE ETERNAL *NIGHT!*

THERE MUST BE *SOME* WAY OUT OF THIS UNEARTHLY PLACE! THERE *MUST* BE!

COME BACK.!! DO YOU THINK YOU CAN EVER ESCAPE FROM HERE? YOU ARE AS MUCH MY CREATION *NOW* AS ANY OF THESE *CREATURES!*

NO! NO! I WON'T BELIEVE IT!

MY FRIEND DOES NOT WANT YOU TO LEAVE. HE WANTS YOU TO *STAY* WITH ME AND CELEBRATE THE TRIUMPH OF *EVIL* OVER *GOOD,* OF *DARK* OVER *LIGHT,* OF *DESPAIR* OVER *HOPE!*

BUT EVIL *DESTROYS* EVIL! YOU WILL SEE!

HOW *DARE* YOU SAY THAT EVIL DESTROYS EVIL! IT *CREATES MORE* EVIL! I SEE THAT I WAS *WRONG* TO BRING YOU HERE!

JULIAN!! YOU'RE *INSANE!* STOP! LET ME GO! ARGHH!

AS HIS ICY FINGERS PRESS AGAINST HER THROAT SEEKING TO STOP ALL BREATH, A MONSTER OF THE SWAMP APPROACHES, HIS SLIMY BODY MATCHED BY THE UGLINESS AND BRUTALITY OF HIS SOUL...

BUT WHY SHOULD I DESTROY YOU? HERE'S ONE OF MY CREATURES-- AND HE CAN DO A MORE *THOROUGH* JOB! CAN'T YOU, MY FRIEND?

I CAN'T *BREATHE!* I CAN'T--!

NO! YOU DON'T UNDERSTAND! NO, *I...* I AM YOUR *FRIEND!* I AM YOUR *DISCIPLE!!* YOU COULDN'T!! NO! NO!!

THE END

MEN FROM MARS

The car's lights jabbed the blackness of the night. Inside the moving car, two men sat quietly watching the dark shadows along the road loom up and then disappear.

"Hey, Joe, how about some music?"

"Sure, Pete.

Suddenly . . .

"WE INTERRUPT THIS BROADCAST TO BRING YOU AN URGENT BULLETIN. AN UNKNOWN OBJECT HAS CRASHED ONTO HIGHWAY 44 TWO MILES OUT OF HICKSVILLE! LIGHT RAYS HAVE BEEN COMING OUT OF THE HOLE THIS OBJECT MADE WHEN IT CRASHED. ALL MOTORISTS ARE WARNED TO GET OFF THE HIGHWAY!!! THE POLICE HAVE BEEN ALERTED. WE NOW CONTINUE 'MUSIC FOR MIDNIGHT.' . . ."

"Did you hear that, Joe? Good heavens! We're on Highway 44 and just three miles from Hicksville!"

"So what!" laughed Joe. "Let's go take a look and see what's it all about. Give us a chance to stretch our legs."

As the car eased around a sharp curve, mysterious beams of light shot into the car!

"Wow! The police must have set up floodlights. This light is blinding!"

Sitting off to one side, Pete wasn't hit fully by the light as was Joe and could see the road. His eyes glazed in horror!

"Joe! Joe! Turn around. Get out of here! There are no police. *It's those THINGS coming out of a hole!* Joe! Swing the car around!"

Horror-stricken, Joe twisted the steering-wheel and sent the car into a skidding turn. Pete plunged his head out of the window to see if the "things" were following them. *"Go, Joe! Go! They're coming after us!"*

Joe's foot crushed the gas pedal. The car raced ahead . . . faster . . . faster! Then, Joe, his forehead glistening with sweat squeezed out by fear, turned to Pete who still had his head out of the window.

"Well, Pete, looks like we made it. Whew! Hey, Pete! Get your head in! PETE!"

Joe pulled at the other man's shoulder. Pete crumpled from the window and sprawled back on the seat. The flesh had been eaten away from his head! Grinning at Joe was a skull!

The fingers of Joe's hands dug into the steering wheel. Joe's body froze into a petrified lump. A grinding noise was coming up behind the car! Biting white light was flooding the car . . . light which gnawed at the flesh of the man hanging on to a car's steering wheel hurtling down a closed highway.

THE BORORO INDIANS OF BRAZIL ARE FIRMLY CONVIN[C]ED THAT IF ANYONE OF THEM TOUCHES MAIZE OR MEAT WH[ICH] HAS NOT BEEN BLESSED BY THE MEDICINE MAN HE AND THE WHOLE TRIBE WILL PERISH.

LOOK, SON OF THE SNAKE. SEE WHAT YOUR EATING OF THE UNBLESSED CORN HAS BROUGHT US!

THE D[...] KILL A [...] HAS KIL[LED] DOES K[...] OF THIS [...] SELVES [...] FIND A [...]

IN AN ANNUAL FIRE-WALKING CEREMONY, THE FIJI-ISLANDERS WALK AND DANCE OVER WHITE-HOT ROCKS. IT IS BELIEVED THAT IF A MAN CAN SAFELY TRAVERSE THE ROCKS, HE IS NOT A SINNER.

USTOMS

IT IS BELIEVED THAT IF A SICK MAN IS REMOVED FROM HIS HOUSE AND A DUMMY PLACED IN HIS BED, INSTEAD, THE DEMON OF SICKNESS WILL MISTAKE THIS DUMMY FOR THE MAN WHO WILL, AS A RESULT, RECOVER.

WILL NOT
S THE BEAST
CROCODILE
ELATIVES
THEM—
TO
R—

HE CROWNING OF A KING OR THE DEDICATION OF A TEMPLE UT, THE AZTECS USED TO SACRIFICE THOUSANDS OF RS FOR EITHER EVENT. THE PRISONERS WERE STRAPPED NE ALTAR WHERE THEIR HEARTS WERE CUT OUT!

CAUGHT!

2 ..3 ..4.. 5...6....7...8....

"Well, operator, we said we wanted 'ten.' Why have you stopped?"

The three men looked at the elevator operator. And, as if one, the breath in their throats stuck when the operator ripped off his disguise!

"That's right, Powell," smiled the operator, "we have stopped. I thought the three of you wouldn't mind stopping a moment and chatting with me. After all, the millions you are making are coming from the invention I invented. Remember how you cheated me . . . killed my brother? Oh, I don't care anymore about the invention but I do care about my brother. *Which one of you killed him?*"

"This is fantastic!" gurgled Roberts.

"Let us out of here, you maniac!" glowered Carter.

"I will! I will," chuckled the operator, "but first I, Charles Corey, once-respected scientist, want to tell you something."

The others in the car pressed closer to its sides.

"The three of you framed me," continued Corey, "and had me cast out of society. You took my work and made yourselves kings. Then, you killed my brother. Now it's my turn . . . to seek justice . . . *my way!*

"Notice that beside each of you there is a button. You see, I arranged you in the elevator when you came in so that one of you now stands over a trap door. I know who the murderer of my brother is. I want him to admit it now. I will give him one minute. If he doesn't speak, I will push a button and the door under him will snap open sending him to his death eight floors below. However, in pushing the button near him, the murderer can jam the door and save himself.

"*The murderer has thirty seconds!*"

As the seconds ticked away, the horror mounted in the minds of the men.

10 seconds...9....8....7....

"NO! NO!"

Roberts couldn't take it. He flung himself at the button and jammed it in! As he did, a trap door swung open and he disappeared down the shaft. The blood curdled in the veins of the other men as they listened to his scream of death!

Finally, Powell found his voice to speak. "You really didn't know who killed your brother, Corey. All three of us were standing over trap doors. You made the killer kill himself!"

"Yes!" smiled Corey, the hard lines of revenge easing out of his face.

"You may call the police."

HOUSE of HORROR

REMEMBER THE TERROR THAT FRANKENSTEIN LOOSED ON HUMANITY WHEN HE GAVE LIFE TO THE *MONSTER.* WELL, THE HOUSE OF HORROR WAS THE BIRTHPLACE OF THIS DEMON!

FROM THIS HOUSE HAVE COME THE MOST HORRIBLE MONSTERS THAT EVER ROAMED THE EARTH! THE WALLS OF THIS HOUSE HAVE TREMBLED TO THE FOOTSTEPS OF THE DEAD AND HAVE SHRIEKED WITH THE SCREAMS OF THE TORTURED LIVING.

OR CAN WE EVER FORGET THE MAN-VAMPIRE *DRACULA!* HOW MANY WHITE, SOFT THROATS FELT HIS SHARP, TEARING TEETH SINK INTO THEM. THE HOUSE OF HORROR WAS *DRACULA'S* HOME!

IN THE DEAD OF NIGHT, WHEN ONLY THE SPIRITS OF SUFFERING SINNERS WALK, ONE CAN HEAR THE SLOW DRAGGING FOOTSTEPS OF A TERROR HORRIBLE ENOUGH TO TURN A MAN TO STONE WITH FEAR! THE *MUMMY!!* AYE, AND THIS MONSTROUS CREATION WALKS IN THE HOUSE OF HORRORS!

AND WHAT ABOUT THE *RIPPER,* THAT MURDERING FIEND WHO CLUTCHED AN ENTIRE CITY IN HIS GRASP OF FRIGHT. MANY WERE THE TIMES WHEN HIS KNIFE RIPPED THROUGH THE AIR AND DUG INTO THE WALLS OF THE HOUSE OF HORROR!

MAN INTO WOLF WHEN THE MOON IS FULL! HOW MANY TIMES HAS A CERTAIN ROOM IN THE HOUSE OF HORROR BEEN THE SCENE OF THIS GRUESOME TRANSFORMATION! HOW MANY TIMES HAS THE *WOLFMAN* BEEN BORN IN IT!

EH? YOU ASK WHAT IS THIS HOUSE OF HORROR? WHERE IS IT? HA-HA! THE HOUSE OF HORROR IS THE *HUMAN MIND!!!*

FERRY OF THE DEAD

NO! NO! *IT CAN'T BE!* GO *AWAY!* AHH-HH-H!

YOUR *DOOM* APPROACHES, DOCTOR! YOU WILL JOIN US IN THE RIVER OF THE DEAD!

NIGHT, AND THE *HIDEOUS* DEMONS THAT *LURK* IN THE DARK CORNERS OF THE EARTH *SLOWLY* EMERGE TO MAKE THEIR HOMES IN THE MINDS OF EVIL MEN...THE *DEAD* AND THE LIVING MEET AT THE FATAL STROKE OF *MIDNIGHT!*

IN THE CASTLE OF DOCTOR KARLA, DEEP IN THE BLACK, BEATING HEART OF ASIA, A *STRANGE* BARGAIN IS COMPLETED...

...AND YOU WILL BRING ME MANY *BODIES* FROM THE GRAVEYARD ON YOUR FERRY, PETERS! I NEED THEM FOR MY EXPERIMENTS, FOR MY CREATION OF A *LIVING HUMAN BODY!!*

KEEP *PAYING* ME AND I'LL KEEP *BRINGING* THEM.!! THERE WON'T BE A *CORPSE* LEFT WHEN I'M DONE!

THIS ONE SEEMS TO BE A *FINE* SPECIMEN!! DOCTOR KARLA WILL BE PLEASED WITH MY WORK!

THERE SHOULD BE ENOUGH BODIES HERE FOR A *DOZEN* EXPERIMENTS! HOW MANY DEAD SOULS ARE *WANDERING* TONIGHT, UNABLE TO REST! WHAT IF THEY SHOULD SEEK *REVENGE??* WHAT IF -- BUT I MUSTN'T THINK OF *THAT!!*

THERE *IT IS!* I'LL HAVE DOZENS OF *ARMS, LEGS* AND *HEADS* WITH WHICH TO COMPLETE MY MASTERPIECE -- MY LIVING, BREATHING *MONSTER!* THE WORLD MUST *NEVER* KNOW -- NOBODY -- BUT WHAT ABOUT *PETERS?* I FORGOT ABOUT *HIM!* HE MUST BE *DESTROYED!!*

A**s A *DREADFUL* CREATURE SPAWNED BY *EVIL* COMES TO FRIGHTENING LIFE, SO A DREADFUL PLAN IS FORMULATED IN AN *EVIL* MIND...

TONIGHT, THE ONE MAN WHO KNOWS OF YOUR EXISTENCE WILL *DIE!* I'LL SNEAK ABOARD HIS SHIP... *HEH! HEH! HEH!*

THERE'S A *STRANGE CHILL* IN THE AIR TONIGHT! THE STENCH OF DEATH IS *EVERYWHERE!* AND I SEEM TO HEAR *VOICES!*

RETURN US TO OUR GRAVES! YOU MUST *RETURN* US TO OUR *G-R-A-V-E-S!*

A**s PETERS BEGAN TO DOCK, KARLA LEAPED ABOARD FROM A LAUNCH AND...

DIE, FOOL! YOU ARE NO USE TO ME ANY LONGER!

WH--"!?

COME BACK, PETERS! YOU WILL *NEVER* ESCAPE FROM THIS BOAT!!

NO! NO! HAVE I NOT SERVED YOU? HAVE MERCY!!

THE VISION OF THE KNIFE ABOVE HIS HEAD, SEEKING TO *RIP* INTO HIS FLESH, THE TERRIFIED PETERS FLEES TO THE CABIN IN WHICH HE HAS PLACED THE *HIDEOUS* BODIES HE HAS STOLEN FROM THEIR GRAVES...

LET ME IN! I WILL NOT BE SATISFIED UNTIL YOUR *BLOOD RUNS* ACROSS THE DECK OF THIS SHIP!

DON'T KILL ME, DOCTOR! DON'T KILL ME!

IF YOU KILL ME, THESE BODIES WILL HAVE ALL THEIR *REVENGE* ON ME FOR *OPENING THEIR GRAVES!* BUT REMEMBER, *YOU* GAVE ME THE *ORDERS!!* YOU...

RAVE ON, FOOL, AND...

DIE!

SINK INTO THE DEPTHS OF THE *DARK RIVER* UNTIL THE WATER TURNS *RED* WITH YOUR *BLOOD!!* YOU ARE AS *DEAD* AS THE BODIES YOU BROUGHT ME! *HEH-HEH-HEH!*

AS THE DAYS PASS, THE *UNHOLY* CREATION OF THE DOCTOR'S *WILD* IMAGINATION BEGINS TO TAKE SHAPE...AND A *NIGHTMARE WORLD* TAKES OVER THE HOUSE ABOVE THE RIVER...

AH, MY PRETTY ONE, YOU ARE FORMING INTO MY *MASTERPIECE* AT LAST! SOON YOU WILL *WALK* AND *BREATHE* -- AND EVEN *SPEAK!* THE BODIES THAT COMPOSE YOU HAVE BEEN *VERY* SATISFACTORY!

THERE'S A FEELING OF DEATH EVERYWHERE TONIGHT! I CAN ALMOST HEAR *TORMENTED SOULS* CALLING TO ME, CALLING TO ME!! *I MUST GO BACK!!*

REVENGE FOR YOUR *STOLEN BODIES!* R-E-V-E-N-G-E!! YOU HAVE VIOLATED THE *PACT OF DEATH!*

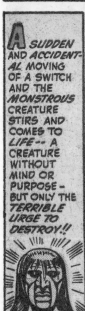

As the GREY DAWN BEGINS TO PENETRATE THE FOUL NIGHT AIR, A STRANGE PROCESSION MOVES SLOWLY AND INEVITABLY TOWARDS THE EDGE OF DOOM AND THE WORLD OF ETERNAL DARKNESS...

FOLLOW ME, UNEARTHLY BEING! JOIN US WHERE ALL UNEARTHLY BEINGS LIVE IN THE PAINFUL FIRE OF ENDLESS DAMNATION!! COME!

MOVE CLOSER TO THE EDGE... CLOSER... CLOSER...

WHERE AM I? N-NO-O! NO! PUT ME DOWN! AH-H-H!

UGHH! EIGHH! AGHH-HH!

I CREATED YOU! I MADE YOU FROM THE CRUMBLING BODIES OF DEAD HUMANS! YOU CAN'T DESTROY ME... AND YOURSELF! NO-O-O!! N...

YAAAAAAAAAAA

NOW YOUR VENGEANCE IS COMPLETE, SPIRITS OF THE DEAD! NOW YOU CAN REST AND MOLD TO DUST IN YOUR DEFILED GRAVES! HE WHO DISTURBED YOUR LONG SLEEP HAS PAID THE TOLL!!

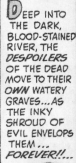

DEEP INTO THE DARK, BLOOD-STAINED RIVER, THE DESPOILERS OF THE DEAD MOVE TO THEIR OWN WATERY GRAVES...AS THE INKY SHROUD OF EVIL ENVELOPS THEM... FOREVER!!...

THE END.

WEIRD WORLDS

MANY PEOPLE THINK THAT THE EARTH HAS BEEN THOROUGHLY EXPLORED. BUT, UNKNOWN TO THEM, THIS PLANET STILL HARBORS PLACES OF MYSTERY... PLACES NO HUMAN HAS EVER SEEN OR WILL EVER SEE!

THERE EXISTS IN THE FROZEN WASTES OF THE NORTH POLE, A CIVILIZATION AS STRANGE AND AS HORRIBLE AS DEATH ITSELF. IN THE FOURTEENTH CENTURY, MARS ATTEMPTED AN INVASION OF THE EARTH BUT ITS ARMIES LANDED ON THE NORTH POLE WHERE THE INTENSE COLD KILLED ALL BUT A FEW OF THE MARTIAN MONSTERS.

BROUGHT BACK TO LIFE BY MAGIC CENTURIES OLD, THE ENTOMBED PHAROAHS OF ANCIENT EGYPT LIVE AND WALK AGAIN IN THEIR PYRAMID GRAVES. EACH PYRAMID IS A CITY OF THE DEAD AND EACH DAY THAT PASSES SEES THESE CITIES GETTING STRONGER AND STRONGER UNTIL...

LOST IN THE JUNGLE OF AFRICA ARE PLANTS WHICH COULD DEVOUR WHOLE BUILDINGS. THEIR STRENGTH IS SUCH THAT THEY COULD WRAP THEMSELVES ABOUT A SKYSCRAPER AND GRIND IT INTO SAND. THEY WOULD THEN GROW AROUND THE REMAINS AND, INSIDE OF A MONTH, COMPLETELY HIDE THEM.

LIVING IN THE BOWELS OF THE EARTH WHERE ROCK AND EARTH SWIRL IN A MOLTEN MASS CAN BE FOUND THE DEMONS WHO GUARD THE GATE TO HELL! EVIL IS THEIR GOD AND FIRE THEIR FOOD!

THE SNAKE MAN

OUT OF THE SIGHT OF MAN CRAWLED A SLIMY, GIANT REPTILE... HUNTED... SHUNNED!!! ONCE ITS DARTING FORKED TONGUE TASTED THE BLOOD OF A HUMAN BEING, THE PUTRID, DEADLY VENOM FLOWED.

HISS-SSS SSS-SSS

STEP RIGHT UP, FOLKS, GET YOUR TICKETS HERE TO SEE *SERPENTINE*, THE *SNAKE-MAN*!! ONLY TEN CENTS, ONE THIN DIME, TO SEE THE WORLD'S GREATEST PHENOMENON! HE *HISSES*, HE *CRAWLS*, HE HAS *SCALES* LIKE A *SNAKE*... BUT HE WAS BORN OF *HUMAN PARENTS*!!

GIMME TWO!

THIS I GOTTA SEE!

AND HERE HE IS, LADIES AND GENTLEMEN, *SERPENTINE*, ONLY ONE OF HIS KIND...

I GUESS WE'LL HAVE TO SEND HIM DOWN ON THE BUS ALONE. HAVE THE DRIVER LOOK AFTER HIM.

YEAH. I'LL PUT A TAG ON HIM, TOO. DON'T KNOW WHY THEY'D WANT HIM AT THE FUNERAL! HE CAN HARDLY TALK!

THE MIND OF THE *SNAKE MAN* IS CONFUSED AS THE VAGUE THOUGHT OF ENTERING THE OUTSIDE WORLD SLOWLY REACHES THE ANIMAL BRAIN...

SERPENTINE, THIS MIGHT NOT MEAN ANYTHING TO YOU, BUT WHEN YOUR MOTHER DIED, HER LAST WISH WAS FOR YOU TO BE AT HER FUNERAL!

YEAH! NOW HERE'S OUR NEXT STOP. PUT IT IN YOUR POCKET AND GET ON THE RIGHT BUS. YOU'RE OUR BEST ATTRACTION AND WE DON'T WANT TO LOSE YOU!

YESSSSS-SSS...

PROPERTY OF BALANTINE BROTHERS CIRCUS. IF LOST, PLEASE REPORT.

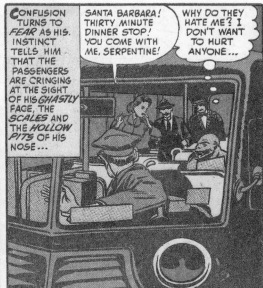

CONFUSION TURNS TO *FEAR* AS HIS INSTINCT TELLS HIM THAT THE PASSENGERS ARE CRINGING AT THE SIGHT OF HIS *GHASTLY* FACE, THE *SCALES* AND THE *HOLLOW PITS* OF HIS NOSE...

SANTA BARBARA! THIRTY MINUTE DINNER STOP! YOU COME WITH ME, SERPENTINE!

WHY DO THEY HATE ME? I DON'T WANT TO HURT ANYONE...

GIVE HIM A HAM SANDWICH AND A MALT. I'LL BE RIGHT BACK.

OH! ALL RIGHT, IF *YOU* SAY SO!

SHE CAN'T STAND TO LOOK AT ME! I WANT TO GO BACK TO THE CIRCUS!

WHAT'S THIS THING SUPPOSED TO BE? UBI, THE BIRD BOY?

NAW, THIS IS SERPENTINE, THE HUMAN REPTILE. WE DON'T LIKE YOU ON THE BUS WITH US, SNAKE EYES!

PROPERTY OF BALANTINE BROTHER'S CIRCUS. IF LOST.

NOW, CRAWL OUT OF HERE, SNAKE-MAN!!

AW, LEAVE THE POOR GUY ALONE!

HISSSST!

LIKE A *CORNERED BEAST*, THE SNAKE-MAN FEELS THAT A *MIND* HIGHER THAN HIS OWN IS *OVERPOWERING* HIM, AND THAT HE MUST *FIGHT* HIS WAY OUT. SOMETHING WITHIN HIM SAYS RUN, *RUN*, *RUN*...

HEY! WHAT'S THE MATTER? *COME BACK!!* NOW YOU'VE DONE IT!!

THAT GUY SHOULDN'T BE LET AROUND LOOSE!

LIKE *DARK, OMINOUS CLOUDS* WHICH *BLOT* OUT THE SUN, *FEAR* AND CONFUSION BESET HIM. USED TO BEING CARED FOR, HE IS LOST AND HELPLESS...

WHERE CAN I GO? WHO WOULD WANT ME?

...BUT SOON THE BALANCE BETWEEN *MAN* AND *BEAST* BEGINS TO SWAY!! SERPENTINE'S EYE HAS *POWER* TO HOLD IN ITS *SPELL* THE CREATURES OF THE FOREST...

FOOD... FOOD! I MUST EAT!

...AND, ALREADY THE WARM BLOOD HAS TURNED *COLD*, COLD AS HIS CHANGING FEELING TOWARD HUMANITY. THE *HORRID VENOM* OOZES FROM *FANGS* NOW LONG AND SHARP...

HISSS! SSSSSST!!

...THE MIND, TOO, GROWS SHARP WITH ALL THE *CRAFT* AND *CUNNING* OF THE SERPENT. AND, LIKE A *GHOUL* UPON A *ROTTING CORPSE,* THE MORE-VIPER-THAN-MAN CREEPS FROM OUT HIS *FETID* HIDING AND *STALKS* IN THE NIGHT...

JIM! I THOUGHT I HEARD SOMETHING! DID... DID YOU HEAR ANYTHING IN THE YARD?

THE ANIMALS HAVE BEEN ACTING UP ALL DAY! I BETTER TAKE A LOOK, MARTHA! PROBABLY A FOX!

WHO... WHO'S THERE? COME OUT OR I'LL SHOOT!

BANG! CRACK!

YAAA! HISSST!!

I'M HIT! I MEANT NO HARM... JUST HUNGRY... NEED FOOD! BUT MAN *HATES* ME! NOW IT'S MY TURN!!

NOW, IN THAT SMALL MIND GROWS A NEW EMOTION -- HATRED! HATRED FOR MAN WHO HAS MADE HIM A SLIMY, CRAWLING FUGITIVE! AND HIS EVIL HEART, POUNDING LIKE GHASTLY CANNIBAL DRUMS, THROBS OUT THE SINGLE THEME: KILL...

KILL!! KILL!! KILL MAN!!

ARMED ONLY WITH THE GRUESOME, HOLLOW FANGS WHICH DRIP THE PUTRESCENT, DEADLY MATTER, THE FOUL, MADDENED FIEND FORGETS HIS FEAR AND LEAVES THE PROTECTIVE FOREST...

AIEEEEE!! ARRRGH!

HELP! HELP!!! EEEEEEEK!!

HUMAN BLOOD... IT'S SWEET TO MY TONGUE!

NOW THAT THE INSANE MONSTER HAS TASTED THE WARM, SWEET HUMAN BLOOD, HE BECOMES A CANNIBAL, THIRSTING FOR MORE, MORE, MORE! AND THIS LUST FOR BLOOD AND VENGEANCE CARRIES HIM TO EVERY CORNER OF THE CITY...

HISSSSST! SSSSSSS!!

LOOK OUT, JOHN! CHILDREN - RUN!

THIS MONSTER MUST BE STOPPED! McCORMICK, GIVE THIS STORY TO THE NEWS-PAPERS! COLLINS, HAVE YOUR DEPARTMENT CARRY OUT THE ORDERS I GAVE YOU!

YES, SIR!

YES, SIR!

RICHARD MILLER
POLICE COMMISSIONER

BULLETIN

SNAKE-MAN BELIEVED HEADING SOUTH; CORDON STRETCHED OVER ALL AREAS

Police everywhere alerted

All asked to cooperate by remaining locked in houses.

SURROUNDED, SERPENTINE *SLITHERS* THRU WOODS, INTO TREES, EAGER TO *KILL*, TO *AVENGE*, TO SINK VENOMOUS FANGS INTO THE THROATS OF MEN...

BOY, I HOPE HE DON'T COME HERE!

IF WE GET HIM, IT'LL MEAN PROMOTION! BUT... BUT WHAT A WAY TO GET STRIPES!

RAT-TAT-TAT-TAT TAT!

GOT TO GET THERE... MUST GO BEFORE IT'S TOO LATE!

LIKE A *GIANT MAGNET* EXERTING ITS *POWER* OVER HIM, THE *GRUESOME* SNAKE-MAN WAS DRAWN ON ALMOST UNCONSCIOUSLY...

KEEP MOVING... GOT TO KEEP MOVING!

THE *HOMING INSTINCT*, STRONG WITHIN HIM, HAS LURED HIM BACK, SEEKING THE SAFETY AND PROTECTION OF HIS OLD HOME...

THEY'LL HIDE ME...THEY'LL PROTECT ME!

HISSSSST! SSSSSSSSS!

AIEEeeee!!

IT...IT'S HIM! HE'S COME TO GET US! HELP!!

SHUNNED! SCORNED BY THOSE WHO HAD CARED FOR HIM, THE FOUL MONSTER'S HATRED INCREASES, AND HIS FINAL LINK WITH HUMANS IS SNAPPED...

THERE HE GOES! GET HIM!

BANG! BANG! CRACK!

I CAN'T HIT HIM! HE WON'T STAY IN ONE PLACE!

AH! I'M HERE... HERE!! HA! HA! REVENGE!

ZOOLOGICAL GARDENS

NOW HIS INSTINCT LED HIM TO THE FETID HOME OF BROTHER MONSTERS...

REPTILE HOUSE

THE GHASTLY CONCLAVE MET TO WREAK HAVOC ON THE MORTAL ENEMY...MAN...

HISSSSSST!! SSSSSSSSS!! RATTLE!

MY BROTHERS! MY FRIENDS! LET... LET US GO AND AVENGE OURSELVES ON THOSE WHO KEEP US DOWNTRODDEN!

QUICK! TO THE REPTILE HOUSE!

TRY NOT TO KILL THE OTHERS IF THEY'RE OUT! WE'LL CATCH THEM ALIVE!!

ZOOLOGICAL GARDENS

ALL WERE FREE BUT THE GIANT MONSTER WHO CURLED WICKEDLY IN THE CORNER, HIS FORKED TONGUE DARTING MENACINGLY...

BROTHER, WE NEED YOUR STRENGTH IN OUR FIGHT. JOIN US AND BE FREE!!

HISSSSSST!

~BOA~ CONSTRICTOR

BUT THE BOA MISTAKES THE *BROTHERLY* GESTURE OF THE SNAKE-MAN...

AHHHHHHH! HISSSSSST!

HE'S ATTACKING! HE WANTS TO CRUSH ME!!

THE TWO LOCKED IN *DEADLY, BESTIAL* COMBAT...THE *POISON* FANGS AGAINST THE *SINISTER,* RIPPLING *MUSCLES*...

WHY DOESN'T HE DIE? I... I CAN'T STAND--MUCH-- MORE!!

OH, GOD! LOOK! ALL THE FIENDS OF HELL ARE LOOSE!

GET BACK! BACK! GET THE SACKS!!!

HISSSSSSST!

OH, NO! IT'S TOO HORRIBLE! HE DIDN'T KNOW THAT POISONOUS AND NON-POISONOUS SNAKES ARE DEADLY ENEMIES, AND THAT NON-POISONOUS SNAKES ARE IMMUNE TO VENOM!

THE END

Chambers of CHILLS

MAN IS FOREVER INVENTING THINGS. AND, SOME OF HIS MOST ACCOMPLISHED INVENTIONS HAVE BEEN THE CHAMBERS HE HAS CONSTRUCTED IN WHICH TO *TORTURE, KILL* AND *BURY* HIMSELF...

IN THE SUN TEMPLES OF ANCIENT SOUTH AMERICA WERE BUILT FANTASTIC ROOMS OF SACRIFICE. IN THE CENTER OF THESE ROOMS, WHERE THE RAYS OF SUNLIGHT COULD STRIKE THEM, WERE PLACED ALTARS OF STONE ON WHICH SACRIFICIAL VICTIMS HAD THEIR HEARTS RIPPED OUT!

IN INDIA, THERE ARE *TOWERS OF SILENCE.* EACH TOWER HAS THREE ROWS IN IT...THE INNERMOST BEING FOR CHILDREN, THE MIDDLE ONE FOR WOMEN AND THE OUTERMOST ROW FOR MEN. YOU SEE, IT IS HERE THAT THE INDIANS BRING THEIR DEAD TO REST! LARGE VULTURES ON THE WALLS FEAST ON THIS BANQUET OF HUMAN FLESH...

IN THE 16TH CENTURY WHEN SHIPS WERE MOVED BY SLAVES WHO PUSHED GIGANTIC OARS FROM THE HOLD OF THE SHIP, DEATH WAS A FREQUENT VISITOR. THESE GALLEY SLAVES HAD TO ROW HUGE SHIPS ACROSS WIDE SEAS AND NEVER WERE ALLOWED TO LEAVE THEIR CHAINS!

MANY OF THE EARLY CHRISTIANS WERE THROWN INTO LION PITS BY THEIR TORMENTORS, THE ROMANS. ONCE INSIDE THE PITS, THE VICTIMS HAD TO FACE SNARLING BEASTS MADE RAVENOUSLY HUNGRY BY NOT BEING FED FOR DAYS!

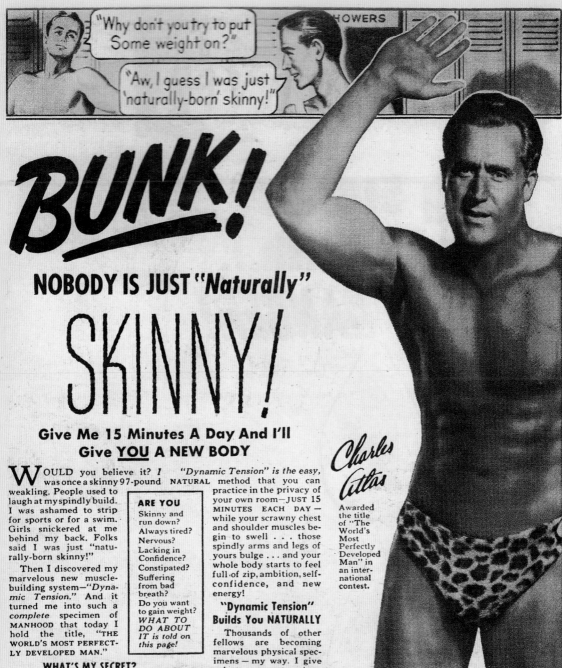

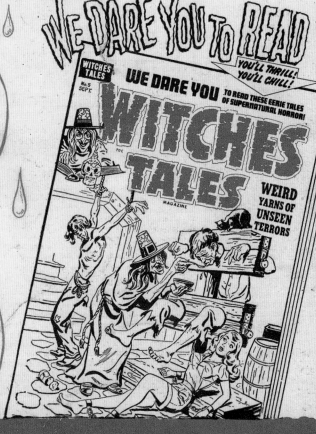

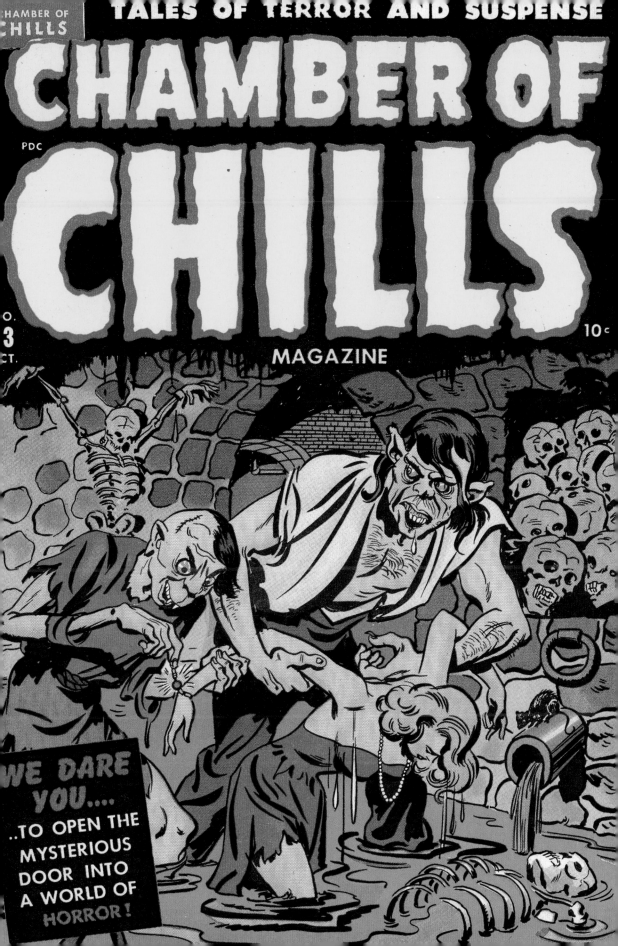

WON'T YOU COME IN?

TABLE OF CONTENTS

CHAMBER OF CHILLS

OCT. No. 23

Once again, the door to the CHAMBER OF CHILLS has opened. Once again, the mystery and the horror of the unknown will be unveiled before your eyes. Once again, your hands will sweat, your spine tingle and your mind teem with thoughts of fear!

In this issue, you will travel through the forbidden tunnels of Crete and meet "The Monster." The walls of your mind will tremble when this "Monster" appears to claim his "victim of the sacrifice."

Then, through the eyes of a man gone mad, you will see THE WALKING DEAD . . . beings dead for five hundred years but cursed to walk the earth forever until they . . .

But we must not forget the masterpiece of psychological horror, TRIP TO TERROR! In that story, YOU will take a TRIP TO TERROR! Yes, you will be on a train going through a tunnel of death. You will see a normal man move five hundred feet—and turn into a raving maniac! Why? Read on and see!

Wait! Prepare yourself for still a fourth adventure into the unknown. Prepare yourself well! In the DOOM OF LIVING ICE, you will be caught in an experience so terrifying as to freeze you on the spot! Ice, thousands of years old, will release the secret of . . . .

Enough! Telling you what to expect is a weak substitute for letting you find out for yourself. Come deeper into the . . .

CHAMBER OF CHILLS

In this issue:

THE DOOM OF LIVING ICE

TRIP TO TERROR

MONSTER'S MAZE

WALKING DEAD

CHAMBER OF CHILLS MAGAZINE, OCTOBER, 1951, Vol. 1, No. 23, IS PUBLISHED EVERY OTHER MONTH by WITCHES TALES, INC., 1860 Broadway, New York 23, N.Y. Application for second class entry pending at the Post Office at New York, N.Y. under the Act of March 3, 1879. Single copies 10c. Subscription rates, 10 issues for $1.00 in the U.S. and possessions, elsewhere $1.50. All names in this periodical are entirely fictitious and no identification with actual persons is intended. Contents copyrighted, 1951, by Witches Tales, Inc., New York City.
Printed in the U.S.A.

FATE SMILED CRUELLY AND OFFERED KURT JENSEN SIGHT FOR BLINDNESS, BUT JENSEN'S EYES BELONGED TO A DEAD MAN AND THROUGH THEM HE KNEW THE TERRIBLE CURSE OF THE...

WALKING DEAD

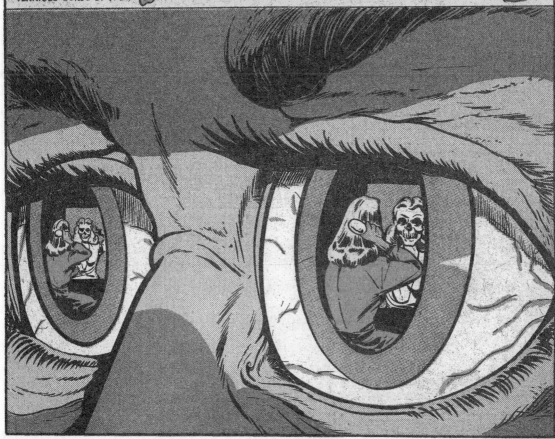

A SCREAM TREMBLED IN KURT JENSEN'S THROAT. WOULD IT BE A SCREAM OF DESPAIR-- OR JOY? YOU SEE, THE HEALTHY EYES OF A DEAD MAN HAD BEEN PLACED IN JENSEN'S SIGHTLESS SOCKETS...

BANDAGES ARE OFF, JENSEN, PRAY--AND OPEN YOUR EYES! CAN YOU SEE--CAN YOU SEE ME, JENSEN?

YES--YES! I CAN SEE! AT LAST I CAN SEE!

JENSEN WAS POSSESSED BY THE SHEER JOY OF SEEING! HE HURLED HIMSELF FROM BED -- DASHED TO A WINDOW---

LOOK -- *LOOK AT IT!* THE CITY! I CAN SEE IT -- *DEAR GOD, I CAN SEE!!*

THEN, SUDDENLY, THE BIG MAN SHIVERED, HIS VOICE PLUNGED FROM JOY TO TERROR---

YAAAA! NO -- *NO!!* TAKE IT AWAY!!

JENSEN -- THE WINDOW -- *LOOK OUT!*

GOOD LORD, MAN! YOU NEARLY WENT OUT THE WINDOW! *WHAT* IS IT?

SOMETHING'S GONE WRONG! THERE'S A HUGE, HIDEOUS COBWEB OVER MY EYES! I SEE -- BUT I SEE THROUGH A MONSTROUS SPIDER'S COBWEB --!!

A COBWEB, YOU SAY? CALM YOURSELF, JENSEN. IT'S JUST AN OPTOTHALMIC REACTION TO THE SURGERY--A HALLUCINATION. IT'LL VANISH IN TWO, THREE WEEKS... WHEN THE SUB-IRIS NERVE-ENDS HEAL.

THE DOCTOR'S WORDS SOOTHED JENSEN'S SUDDEN FRIGHT. DAYS PASSED, AND A MAN, ONCE BLIND, NOW WALKED WITH THE FREEDOM OF SIGHT--- SIGHT THROUGH A DEAD MAN'S EYES...

GLAD T'SEE YOU AGAIN, MR. JENSEN! I'M SURE GLAD THE SAWBONES FIXED YOU UP WITH NEW PEEPERS!

THANKS, GEORGE. GIVE ME A QUICK ONE.

THE COBWEB! ALWAYS THERE! IF ONLY -- *ONLY* -- IT WOULD GO AWAY --!

THAT CASTLE! DON'T TRICK ME, GEORGE! TAKE THAT PICTURE OF A CASTLE AWAY!

CASTLE? *WHAT* CASTLE, MR. JENSEN --?

A VISION HAD SNAPPED INTO FOCUS BEFORE JENSEN'S EYES. THE VISION WAS A CRUMBLING, FRIGHTENING STRUCTURE, INCONGRUOUSLY PLACED AGAINST THE MODERNITY OF THE SEVENTH AVENUE BAR!

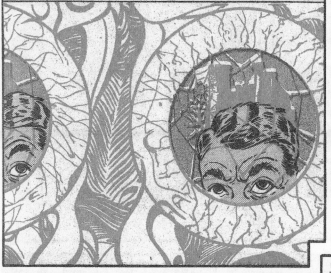

IT'S TOO MUCH--¡GASP!-- FIRST THE COBWEB--THEN-- THE CASTLE! I CAN'T STAND IT--¡GASP!-- I CAN'T STAND IT!

POOR GUY - HE'S GOIN' OFF HIS NUT. BRRR-- WHAT A FUNNY LOOK IN THOSE NEW EYES OF HIS...LIKE THE EYES OF A-- A DEAD MAN!

FRANTIC, JENSEN SOUGHT OUT THE DOCTOR WHO HAD GIVEN HIM A DEAD MAN'S EYES THAT HE MIGHT SEE AGAIN--

A CASTLE--YES, A CASTLE! IS *THAT* A HALLUCINATION, TOO? OR-- OR DOES IT HAVE SOMETHING TO DO WITH THE MAN WHO-- WHO *FIRST HAD* *THESE EYES*--?

WHAT? COME, COME, MR. JENSEN! HA-HA-HA-HA---

BY LAW, JENSEN, I CAN'T TELL YOU WHOSE EYES YOU HAVE. HOWEVER, THE THOUGHT THAT A PERSON IS HAUNTING YOU THROUGH YOUR NEW EYES IS SHEER FANTASY. THESE VISIONS ARE MERELY REACTIONS OF YOUR OPTIC NERVES. WHY DON'T YOU TAKE A VACATION--TAKE A GOOD REST--

LATER, THE DOCTOR STOOD ALONE WITH HIS THOUGHTS- TREMBLING!

IT'S FANTASTIC! JENSEN'S EYES CAME FROM A SPANISH NOBLEMAN KILLED IN A PLANE CRASH AT THE CITY AIRPORT... AND THAT CASTLE JENSEN DESCRIBED-- I'D SWEAR IT WAS A *SPANISH* CASTLE! BUT IT CAN'T BE--- IT--CAN'T--BE--!

MEANWHILE, JENSEN, TENSE AS TAUT RUBBER, WALKED GRIMLY, EVEN WILDLY, TO THE NEAREST TRAVEL BUREAU...

ALL RIGHT--I'LL LEAVE! NOW-- *TODAY*! ANYTHING--ANYTHING TO SEE *CLEARLY* AGAIN...

YESSIR. HELP YOU? NOT YET, I DON'T KNOW WHERE I WANT TO GO. ALL THESE FOLDERS--THESE DIFFERENT PLACES--I'LL JUST PICK ONE OUT, ANYWHERE---

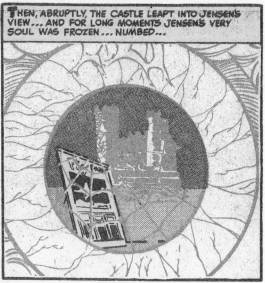

THEN, ABRUPTLY, THE CASTLE LEAPT INTO JENSEN'S VIEW... AND FOR LONG MOMENTS JENSEN'S VERY SOUL WAS FROZEN... NUMBED...

THEN, QUICKLY, IT VANISHED... AND JENSEN HEARD THE CLERK SPEAK TO HIM...

WHAT--? TICKETS? WHAT TICKETS?

WHY, SIR, YOU JUST ORDERED TICKETS ON A PLANE TO SPAIN, DON'T YOU WANT THEM?

I MUST'VE ORDERED THEM WHEN THAT-- THAT HIDEOUS CASTLE BLINDED ME.

AH--YES. SPAIN'S ALL RIGHT--AS GOOD A PLACE AS ANY FOR A VACATION. YES, YES. I'LL TAKE THEM...

OH, BROTHER! THAT GUY SHOULD HAVE A ONE-WAY TICKET TO THE LOONEY-BIN-- NOT SPAIN! BRRR--WHAT EYES! LIKE FROZEN BLOOD!

IN SPAIN, JENSEN FOUND NO REST. IN FACT, THE VISIONS GOT WORSE! THEN, HIS MIND STRAINED TO THE LIMIT, JENSEN SOUGHT RELIEF... IN DEATH!

I SWORE I'D KILL MYSELF IF THE OPERATION WASN'T SUCCESSFUL. AND NOW--NOW I'D RATHER BE DEAD THAN SEE THROUGH THIS CURSED COBWEB--AND I SHALL BE DEAD! JUST A BIT OF SPEED-- A CRASH--HA-HA-HA-HA--!

BUT FATE HELD HORROR, NOT DEATH, IN STORE FOR JENSEN. JUST AS HE BEGAN TO SPEED, THE SKY SPLIT OPEN AND--

THE LIGHTNING STUNNED BOTH JENSEN AND THE CAR. THE MOTOR CHOKED OFF. JENSEN'S FURY FLARED UP TO MATCH THAT OF THE RAGING STORM ABOVE...

CURSE IT, *CURSE IT!* I CAN'T EVEN KILL MYSELF! I'M TO *SUFFER,* NOT *DIE,* IS THAT IT? HA-HA-HA-HA-HA--- *SUFFER*--HA-HA-HA-- *S-U-F-F-E-R*---

BUT JENSEN STRANGLED HIS MANIACAL SCREAMS WHEN HE SAW SOMETHING MOVING AT THE ROAD'S EDGE...

A WOMAN--IN THIS GODFORSAKEN WILDERNESS! WAIT--WAIT! DON'T LEAVE!

WAIT! I'M LOST--¿GASP¿--IN THIS STORM! ¿GASP¿ IN THIS DARKNESS --¿GASP¿-- IT LOOKS LIKE SHE'S FLOATING --¿GASP¿-- NOT WALKING--MAYBE SHE COULD HELP ME!

JENSEN RACED THROUGH THE WOODED DARKNESS AND STINGING RAIN, UNTIL---

YAAAAA! THE CASTLE! THE CASTLE I'VE BEEN SEEING -- *THERE IT IS--* AND IT'S REAL!

JENSEN FELL HEAVILY TO THE GROUND AND LAY AS IF DEAD. SOON THERE CAME A SIGH AND A FAINT RUSTLE. THE GRAVE'S DAMP ODOR SWELLED FORTH AS BESIDE A GNARLED, STORM-SEARED TREE THERE APPEARED THREE FIGURES...

HE IS HERE, SISTER. THE MORTAL WITH OUR BROTHER'S EYES--

COME...COME, LET US TAKE HIM TO ETERNITY'S TOMB.

A DIM, VAGUE CONSCIOUSNESS FILTERED THROUGH JENSEN. HE FELT HIMSELF MOVING...FLOWING...FLOATING...AND, THEN, HE FELT THE NEED FOR SLEEP...ENDLESS SLEEP.

LIGHTS, SHADOWS, AND SOUNDS GLIMMERED AND DIED IN JENSEN'S MIND...AND THEN HE FELT A COLD HAND PRESS HIS ARM...

NOW...TO MAKE HE-WITH-OUR-BROTHER'S EYES ONE OF US...BY GIVING HIM THE TOUCH OF...THE UN-DEAD...

MAKE HASTE... THE BREATH OF DAWN HOVERS... WE MUST RETURN... TO THE DEAD...

HOURS LATER, JUST AS THE HAZE OF TWILIGHT SLITHERED OVER THE MOUNTAINS, JENSEN AWOKE...

THAT'S FUNNY--THERE'S NO COBWEB OVER MY EYES NOW! OHH...WHERE AM I? WAS I DREAMING, OR WERE THOSE TWO GIRLS--THAT GIANT DOG-- *REAL*? OHH....MY HEAD...

WHY--THIS IS A--A TOMB! AND--THAT-- COBWEB! IT'S THE COBWEB I'VE BEEN *SEEING!* IT'S REAL--IT'S REAL!

THE GIRLS--I DID SEE THEM! DEAD IN THIS DUST AND DECAY-- LOOKING AS FRESH AS LIFE! I--I MUST BE MAD--STARK RAVING MAD---

SUDDENLY, JENSEN WAS NO LONGER A MAN...BUT AN ANIMAL, CRAZED WITH FEAR, SPURRED BY TERROR...

YAAAA--LET ME OUT--*LET ME OUT OF HERE!!!*

HA-HA-HA-HA--I'M ONE OF THEM NOW! A GHOUL--A GHOST! I DIDN'T BREAK THE COBWEB WHEN I RAN THROUGH IT! HA-HA-HA! A GHOUL---I'M A GHOUL---HA-HA-HA-HA--

SOBBING, SCREAMING, JENSEN RAN OUT OF THE CASTLE, DOWN A ROAD...AND THE DARKNESS PRESSED IN ON HIM LIKE THE JAWS OF A VISE...

EEEEEEEEE--

GRANDFATHER--LOOK! AN UN-DEAD ONE FROM THE CASTLE!

JENSEN FELL...GIBBERING CRAZILY...

YAAAAA--

HA-HA-HA--¿GASP¿--I'M DEAD--BUT YOU--WHY DON'T YOU RUN, TOO, OLD MAN--¿GASP¿--

I AM TOO OLD, SEÑOR. DEATH CANNOT FRIGHTEN ONE WHO WAITS FOR HIM!

OLD MAN... I WON'T HURT YOU--JUST TELL ME WHAT--OR WHO--YOU THINK I AM! THAT GIRL--SHE CALLED ME "UN-DEAD"--WHAT DID SHE MEAN? WHAT DID SHE MEAN--?

YOU DO NOT KNOW? BUT--I DO AS YOU ASK, SO THAT I MAY DIE IN PEACE, AND NOT PROVOKE YOUR UN-DEAD CURSE...

THE CASTLE HAS BEEN EMPTY OF LIFE FOR CENTURIES... BUT NOT EMPTY OF THE UN-DEAD ONES. FIVE HUNDRED YEARS AGO, COUNT KRULL GRIMM AND HIS TWO SISTERS LIVED IN THE CASTLE. ONE NIGHT, THEY INVITED NEIGHBORING NOBILITY TO DINE WITH THEM--

"BUT THEY INVITED THEM TO DINE ON DEATH--NOT FOOD. COUNT GRIMM AND HIS SISTERS MURDERED THEIR GUESTS--TO GET THEIR FORTUNES..."

SWINE--¿GASP?--I DOOM YOU--WITH THE CURSE OF THE UN-DEAD. ¿GASP?--FOR WHEN YOU DIE--YOU SHALL BE DEAD ONLY IN THE DAY--¿GASP?--AT NIGHT YOU SHALL WANDER AS UN-DEAD ONES--¿GASP?--AND 500 YEARS FROM TONIGHT, ONLY IF YOU ARE ALL HERE--¿GASP?--WILL MY CURSE BE LIFTED--

BUT--¿GASP?--IF YOU ARE NOT HERE 500 YEARS FROM THIS BLOODY NIGHT ¿GASP?--THEN YOU SHALL NEVER KNOW DEATH--¿GASP?--BUT SHALL WANDER UN-DEAD FOREVER--¿GASP?--

ARE YOU THROUGH, IDIOT? THEN DIE-- AND TAKE YOUR FILTHY CURSE WITH YOU--- HA-HA-HA-HA---

BUT HE DID NOT "RAVE", FOR THE CURSE CAME TRUE. FOR CENTURIES COUNT GRIMM AND HIS SISTERS HAVE WANDERED OVER THE EARTH AT NIGHT--THE WALKING DEAD.

BUT ME! WHAT ABOUT ME? WHAT HAVE I-- "EYE"! THEY GAVE ME THE COUNT'S EYES-- AND I, TOO, AM--- AM UN-DEAD!!

ARRRGGG...YOUR FRIENDS, SEÑOR--BEHIND YOU-- YOUR FRIENDS--- ARRRGGG...

YOU! YOU--- COUNT KRULL GRIMM...

GOOD EVENING, SEÑOR. WE MEET AT LAST. AND I HAVE COME FOR MY EYES!

THE FOOLS TOOK MY EYES AND GAVE THEM TO YOU AFTER THAT PLANE CRASH. THE CRASH CAME IN DAYLIGHT SO THEY THOUGHT THE CRASH KILLED ME WHEN I SHOWED NO SIGNS OF LIFE!

THEY SHIPPED MY EYELESS BODY HOME. IT ARRIVED TODAY. BUT I--MY SPIRIT-- LEFT THE BODY AND CAME TO YOU--- AND FORCED YOU HERE-- SO THAT I MIGHT CLAIM MY EYES-- MY EYES! MY EYES!

NO. NO-- DON'T COME ANY NEARER--

GIVE THEM TO ME! FOR TONIGHT IS THE NIGHT THE CURSE ENDS-- BUT ONLY IF WE ARE IN THE CASTLE, WHOLE AND ENTIRE! GIVE BACK MY EYES!

NO--NO! DON'T! I-- YAAAAAAA-A-A.

THE DANKNESS OF THE GRAVE, OF DEATH ITSELF, SWEPT OVER JENSEN AND, IN A FINAL SWOON OF TERROR, HE BLACKED OUT. HOURS LATER, WHEN HE AGAIN AWOKE--

CAN'T SEE-- CAN'T SEE-- MY EYES--GONE. A SKULL! I FEEL-- A SKULL---

HA-HA-HA-HA! I'M IN THE TOMB AGAIN--AND THEY'RE SKELETONS--THEY'RE DEAD FOREVER NOW! HA-HA-HA-HA--THEY TOOK MY EYES AND THE CURSE ENDED!

BUT ME--ME! I'M BLIND AGAIN--AND I'M UN-DEAD! I'M--WHAT--I'M TEARING IT, I'M TEARING THE WEB!! I'M HUMAN AGAIN! THEY LEFT ME HUMAN!!

A BLINDING JOY AND EXULTATION SURGED OVER JENSEN! IT DID NOT MATTER THAT HE WAS BLIND AGAIN!

I TORE THAT COBWEB--TORE IT! HA-HA-HA--! I'M REAL--- I'M WHOLE! HA-HA-HA-HA---I'M BLIND---BUT I'M FREE--- FREE--FREE--FREE---

FREE

FREEEE

FREE!

FREE!

FREE

THE END

HALL OF HORROR!

The moon was blood red. The occasional clouds that ran across the face of it rippled the redness and made the moon appear to expand and contract. Below, on earth, a certain house was bathed in lunar light. The large shingle above the doorway groaned back and forth as a slight wind stirred. When the sign swung out into the moonlight, large, black letters announced, "PROFESSOR DRAK'S HALL OF HORROR."

Then, from inside the building . . . "Aiehh! Argghhh! Sto-o-o-o-op!"

On the second floor, a scene of sanity-searing terror was taking place. Strapped to a medieval torture table was a man. Digging into him, from a bar above, were rows of razor sharp spikes! And, standing off to one side, Professor Drak was laughing madly as he moulded the expression of the dying man onto a clay bust.

"Yell, yell, you fool! Let the lines in your face twist with pain and horror. Yes, when the stupid art critics come to see my latest masterpiece they will say again, 'Why, Professor, you are a master sculptor. How can you get such real expression into your work?' The fools!"

By now, the man on the table had died. Drak lifted the torn body and dragged it to a trap door. When he opened the door, he was met with the savage grunts of crocodiles!

"Here, my pretties, feast on another of my 'models.' Too bad he had to die so soon. He was quite good!" He rolled the corpse into the pit. As he closed the door, there could be heard cracking noises as if bone were being crushed by tremendous vises!

* * *

Months had passed. Professor Drak was now acclaimed the greatest sculptor of all time. His works were exact, detailed and real. No one knew how he did it.

Then, it happened! Professor Drak's mind began to shatter with thoughts of self-worship. Everyone said he was a genius. Honors were being heaped on him. The world was his!

"I am the greatest genius ever known. But, I have not yet created my masterpiece."

The professor's eyes, now grown wild with madness, swept over the work room.

"Yes, I have yet to create my masterpiece. I have yet to do 'Laughing At Death'!"

Slowly, the man rose from his chair. Carefully, he placed all his instruments and materials alongside a long table. Above this table was raised the same bar of spikes which had murdered the man before. Professor Drak adjusted the mirror which hung beside the bar. Then, he stretched himself on the table!

He flicked a switch. Hydraulic motors began to lower the spiked bar . . . a fraction of an inch at a time! The professor began to mould the bust by his side. He would look into the mirror and then add a stroke to the bust.

The spikes kept getting closer.

"Aha, I will mould my laughing expression as I stare death in the face. Then, how those fools will marvel. But, just before the spikes reach my skin, I will stop the bar. Ha-a-a-a-a-!"

The spikes were very close. Drak was almost finished. He was moulding an expression of confidence . . . laughing at death!

Closer and closer came the points of death. Faster and faster worked Drak.

"Just a little more . . . ah . . . it is done! Now to stop the bar . . . Wh . . . I . : . STOP! STOP!"

The motors would not stop. Though the man, lost in desperation, jammed the switch back and forth, the spiked bar kept on coming . . . coming . . . coming!

"No . . . I cannot die . . . I must live . . . I . . . arghhhh . . ."

The points began to slowly sink into Drak's flesh. His heart pounded savagely. Deeper . . . deeper . . . deeper, crept the spikes. The man's arms moved convulsively at his side. Sheer horror had clamped his jaws and he couldn't even scream!

The points were touching the wall of Drak's heart!

Then, in a last violent sweep of his right arm, Drak accidentally struck the bust. His clawing fingers raked across the face.

"ARRRGHHHH!"

Death had come!

Later, when the police had left the house after making their examinations, Inspector Grange turned to his aide and said, "It's a funny thing, Wilks!"

"What's that, sir?"

"That bust was named 'Laughing at Death,' wasn't it?"

"That's what the sign under it said."

"Well, if he was mad enough to kill himself so he could mould his own face laughing at death, why did he end up by putting a look of horror on the bust?"

"Yeah, you're right, inspector. Those streaks across the bust did give the thing a terrified look . . . Oh, well, I guess that's the way he wanted it to look!"

TRIP TO TERROR

PERKINS WAS A *MILD, MEEK* LITTLE MAN - EVERYBODY ALWAYS *SHOVED* HIM AROUND! BUT PEOPLE SOMETIMES FORGET THAT *POISON* COMES IN *SMALL PACKAGES!* ONE DAY, PERKINS DECIDED HE HAD ENOUGH, AND SO BEGAN HIS...

KEEP BACK! KEEP AWAY FROM ME...YOU *FIEND!!*

FOR *TWENTY-TWO YEARS* PERKINS HAD WORKED BEHIND THE SAME DESK FOR THE SAME COMPANY! HE NEVER *COMPLAINED* - EVEN WHEN...

SO THE BOSS WANTS THOSE REPORTS CHECKED, HUH? WELL, GIVE 'EM TO PERKINS - HE'S THE *WORK-HORSE* AROUND HERE!

YES, MR. DOOLEY!

C'MON, PERKINS-TIME TO QUIT! DON'T WANT TO MISS THE TRAIN, DO YA?

(COUGH-COUGH!) BE RIGHT ALONG-JUST A FEW MORE MOMENTS...

PARDON ME... PLEASE... PARDON M--OOOFF!

GANGWAY! LEMME THRU! C'MON, PERKINS--*SHOVE!* HOW D'YOU EXPECT TO GET ANYWHERE IN THIS WORLD IF YOU DON'T *PUSH!?*

YES... TWENTY-TWO YEARS OF BEING STEPPED ON, BRUISED AND BATTERED BY PEOPLE TWICE HIS SIZE!

WHERE'S THAT LITTLE GUY TONIGHT?

WHO, PERKINS? OH, LOST IN THE CROWD SOMEWHERE, AS USUAL! DEAL 'EM!

WHY IS IT YOU'RE ALWAYS THE *LAST ONE* OFF THE TRAIN?? *EVERY NIGHT* YOU HOLD US UP!!

SORRY, SIR... IT'S JUST THAT I DON'T LIKE TO SHOVE PEOPLE... I...

BUT *DEEP INSIDE* THE LITTLE MAN THERE BEGAN TO GROW, AFTER ALL THESE YEARS, A TIGHT KNOT OF *BITTERNESS!* HE SUDDENLY WANTED TO *STRIKE BACK!!* THE NEXT DAY...

HERE SHE COMES... STAND BACK, PERKINS...

OW! DOOLEY, QUIT SHOVING!!

THE *SERENE BALANCE* OF THE LITTLE MAN'S BRAIN BECAME MOMENTARILY UPSET-- AS *UNBALANCED* AS DOOLEY WHEN HE SUDDENLY FOUND HIMSELF TOPPLING FORWARD...

PERKINS... DON'T *PUSH* ME!! DON'T...!!

SCREEEE-EE

NO! THE POOR GUY... MUST'VE SLIPPED!

I DID IT!! BUT I DIDN'T MEAN TO... TO *KILL* HIM! I JUST GOT MAD... I JUST WANTED A *LITTLE ROOM!* OHHHHH...

AIEEEEE

BUT *NOBODY* HAD SEEN PERKINS SEND DOOLEY HURTLING TO HIS *DEATH* IN THE CROWDED STATION! LATER, AS HE WALKED HOME, THE *COOL BREEZE* CARESSED HIM LIKE A *GHOSTLY HAND*...

...IT...IT'S LIKE A NIGHTMARE!! MAYBE I DIDN'T *REALLY* DO IT!! MAYBE I JUST *THINK* I DID! WHY, SURE- DOOLEY SLIPPED BY HIMSELF...

BUT THE MIND OF THE LITTLE MAN WAS *UNEASY!* THAT NIGHT, HE WOKE SUDDENLY IN A *COLD SWEAT,* AND THE SHEETS WERE *CLAMMY,* LIKE A *DAMP SHROUD*...

HUH? WH-- *WHO ARE YOU?!* HOW...HOW DID YOU GET IN HERE?! KEEP BACK... *KEEP BACK!!*

WH...WHERE ARE YOU *ALL* COMING FROM!!? DON'T TOUCH ME WITH THOSE...THOSE *ROTTING FINGERS!* AHHHHHH...!

LET ME GO.... *LET ME GO!!* I DIDN'T DO ANYTHING! I...I'VE GOT TO *GET OUT OF HERE!!*

GLARGHSHGH...

R-RIP!

WITH FINGERS THAT *WRITHE* LIKE *TORTURED WORMS,* THE HANDS OF THE *MIDNIGHT DEMONS* REACH TO *PLUCK* AT PERKINS' *EYES;* TO *TEAR* AT HIS *THROAT!* THEN, WITH *INSANE ENERGY*...

AHHHHHHH!!

CRASH!

HE RAN WITH THE WINGS OF *FEAR* AT HIS ANKLES! INTO THE *BLACK NIGHT* HE PLUNGED, *WAILING* LIKE A *BANSHEE DOOMED TO ETERNAL FLIGHT!!* FINALLY...

NOW THERE, MISTER-- WHAT'S ALL THE SCREAMING AND RUNNING ABOUT??

THEY'RE AFTER ME...S...S... *SAVE ME! DOOLEY* MUST'VE *SENT THEM!* THEY WANT TO...TO...K-K-*KILL ME!!*

BUT... BUT I TELL YOU, OFFICER-THEY *ATTACKED* ME! LOOK -- THEY TORE MY PAJAMAS!

THERE'S *NO ONE* HERE! I THINK YOU'VE HAD A *BAD NIGHTMARE*, MR. PERKINS...GO BACK TO BED...

TO PERKINS, EVERY *SOUND* DURING THE REST OF THE NIGHT SEEMED THE FOOTSTEP OF A *RETURNING DEMON!!* NEXT DAY, HE HOPED *DOOLEY WOULD APPEAR* AT THE OFFICE AS USUAL- THAT THE WHOLE THING HAD BEEN A *FANTASY!* BUT...

DID YOU HEAR ABOUT POOR, OLD DOOLEY? *HORRIBLE...*

YES... WHAT A *TERRIBLE ACCIDENT!* MAKES MY *BLOOD RUN COLD* JUST TO THINK ABOUT IT!!!

HE *IS* DEAD!! BUT... BUT NOBODY KNOWS I DID IT. .!!

THAT EVENING, ON THE TRAIN HOME...

YOU'RE PERKINS, AREN'T YOU? DOOLEY...AH... USED TO TALK ABOUT YOU...

NOW THAT POOR, OLD DOOLEY'S GONE, WE'LL NEED A FOURTH FOR PINOCHLE EVERY DAY... HOW ABOUT YOU, PERKINS?

ME? WELL, SURE- AND I'LL BE ABLE TO HAVE A SEAT EVERY DAY, WON'T I?! HEE-HEE-HEE!

AS THE *ROARING* TRAIN GOES SWEEPING AROUND A CURVE, THE LIGHTS *BLINK OUT* FOR A FEW, BRIEF SECONDS - AND PERKINS SITS GRINNING, A *WEIRD* LITTLE GRIN- THE GRIN OF A MAN WHO KEEPS A *BLACK SECRET*...

THE LIGHTS *FLICKER* BACK ON... AND WHEN PERKINS LOOKS AROUND, WHAT HE SEES MAKES HIS EYEBALLS *WITHER* IN THEIR SOCKETS!

YES.... WE WERE *DOOLEY'S FRIENDS FOR YEARS*, YOU KNOW...

WHAT'S THE MATTER, PERKINS? PLAY YOUR CARDS...!

NO.... NO!! THEY'RE *BACK!!* HELP! HELP! CONDUCTOR...

WHAT'S THE TROUBLE, MR. PERKINS? ANYTHING WRONG??

A!EEE-EEE-EEE!

WITH SUDDEN, *MANIACAL FURY*, THE LITTLE MAN STRIKES BACK WITH ARMS NOW LIKE *THIN WHIPS!* BUT THE *DEMONS STALK HIM RELENTLESSLY...*

I'LL *KILL* YOU!! I'LL *KILL* ALL OF YOU... JUST THE WAY I *KILLED* DOOLEY!! HA-HA-HA-HA!!

GLARGHGHRJGH!

YOU *WON'T* GET *ME!!* HA-HA....!

ARRRGHGH!

O!EEEE....!

BUT THERE IS *NO ESCAPE* ON THE *ROARING TRAIN* THAT HURTLES THROUGH THE *BLACK TUNNEL!* PERKINS HAS RUN OUT OF WEAPONS, AND THRU THE *WIDENING CRACK* IN HIS *BRAIN*, HIS *CONSCIOUSNESS RUNS OUT....!!*

KEEP AWAY...KEEP AW....AAAAAHH!!

HERE HE IS, OFFICER... HE WENT *WILD* AFTER THE LIGHTS FLICKED ON IN THE TUNNEL! WE'VE HAD A TIME SUBDUING HIM!

POOR DOOLEY MOULDERING IN HIS *GRAVE*....HA-HA-HA! ARE YOU COMFORTABLE, DOOLEY? HAVE YOU *GOT ENOUGH ROOM NOW?* HA-HA-HA!!

Drink GRAPE SQUASH

SOMEWHERE IN THE *BLACK TUNNEL* PERKINS *LOST HIS SANITY*— CUT AWAY BY THE SHARP KNIFE OF *GUILT!!* NOW *HE SEES THINGS* WE DO NOT SEE, *HEARS* WHAT WE DO NOT HEAR...

HEE-HEE! I *SEE* YOU, DOOLEY... HOW DO YOU LIKE *BEING DEAD*, DOOLEY? YOU KNOW— I KILLED YOU.... HEE-HEE-HEE!

BOY, THIS GUY HAS *REALLY* BLOWN HIS TOP!!

CAREFUL, MEN— HE'S A *DANGEROUS KILLER!!*

THE END.

Brain Operation!

"Doctor, what do you think?"

"I don't know, Adams. I never had a case like his before. If I had but faltered for an instant, he would have died. The bullet was touching the brain."

"What happened to the crook who shot him?"

"I understand the police have him, Adams. And I don't think they're going to treat him too well. After all, he did shoot a policeman ... maybe killed him. One can never be sure of a brain operation."

Just then, Patrolman Richards was wheeled from the operating room.

Doctor Rice stopped the table. He bent over the wounded man.

"Good heavens, Adams, he's opening his eyes! Quick, get me the hypodermic needle!"

As Adams rushed away, Patrolman Richards began to get up!

"Ahhh! Arggh!"

"Lie down, Richards. You're all right. Don't get ... ohhh!"

Richards had smashed his fist into Rice's face, knocking the doctor down.

"Oh no," gasped Rice, "the operation has affected his brain ... made him a madman."

Richards staggered down the hall, his body stiff with madness. But fate has a funny way of handling things. Down at the other end of the hall, a small girl, visiting her sick father, had wandered out on a platform for open air patients. She had a little ball with her. As she bounced it, the ball skipped away and towards the edge.

At that moment the policeman saw the girl. Somewhere, lost in the whirling confusion of his damaged mind, an experience was remembered. He had helped children cross streets. He knew children. He ...

With a warning shout, the madman made for the little child. There was danger. The child, only thinking of her ball, would never stop herself in time from falling over the edge.

But, with a mighty sweep, the wounded officer pulled the child back, held her for a moment, then fell back with her to safety.

When the doctors reached Richards and the child, they grew silent. The little girl was telling the officer to wake up. The strain of saving the child had been too much for the man. He was dead.

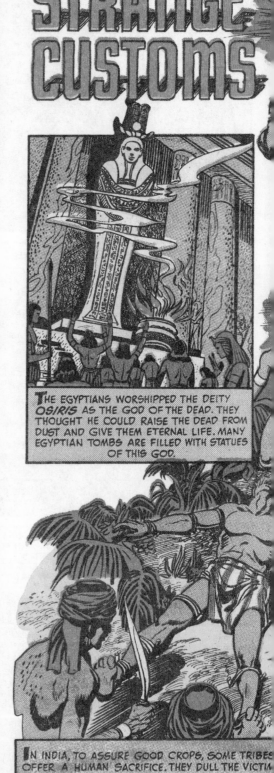

STRANGE CUSTOMS

THE EGYPTIANS WORSHIPPED THE DEITY *OSIRIS* AS THE GOD OF THE DEAD. THEY THOUGHT HE COULD RAISE THE DEAD FROM DUST AND GIVE THEM ETERNAL LIFE. MANY EGYPTIAN TOMBS ARE FILLED WITH STATUES OF THIS GOD.

IN INDIA, TO ASSURE GOOD CROPS, SOME TRIBES OFFER A HUMAN SACRIFICE. THEY DULL THE VICTIM'S SENSES WITH OPIUM THEN PROCEED TO HACK THE FLESH AWAY FROM HIS BODY UNTIL DEATH COM...

OME TRIBES OF NORTH AMERICAN INDIANS, IT WAS
HAT YOUNG BRAVES WHO HAD TAKEN THEIR FIRST
RE BOUND TO OBSERVE CERTAIN CEREMONIES. IF
, THE GHOST OF THE MAN THEY KILLED WOULD
D WORK THEIR DEATH BY MAGIC.

IS BELIEVED IN CORNERS OF THIS EARTH THAT
WITCH CAN TAKE A SICKNESS FROM ONE
RSON AND TRANSFER IT TO ANOTHER. HER BLACK
GIC VARIES WITH THE SICKNESS!

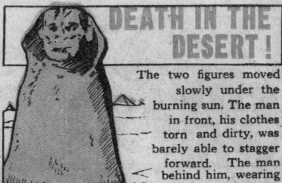

DEATH IN THE DESERT !

The two figures moved slowly under the burning sun. The man in front, his clothes torn and dirty, was barely able to stagger forward. The man behind him, wearing the uniform of the French Foreign Legion, had almost caught up to him.

The first man dropped!

In minutes, the legionnaire was standing over the fallen man . . . gloating . . .

"So, William Driggs, you thought you could escape from the Legion. Did you not know that the Legion always brings back the deserters . . . especially if Sergeant Rimbaud is sent after them . . . eh?"

"Let me alone, you devil! I cannot take your abuses anymore. You drove me from the Legion!"

"Oh, *I* drove you away, eh? Well, you're soft and weak. It gave me great pleasure to torture you. I hate weakness . . . But enough talk. Strip off your shirt and throw it here!"

"But why, Rimbaud? I'll need it to go back."

"Do as I say, dog!"

Driggs took off his shirt and threw it towards Rimbaud.

"I made you give me your shirt because it will be evidence that I caught you. You see, I intend to kill you—just as you tried to kill me at that last waterhole. My horse drank the poisoned water first. It died. Ha-Ha . . . I just have enough water to get back myself. Do you think I would take you, then? Here, dog, look at this canteen. Look, I'll open it. See the cool water in it."

As Rimbaud held the canteen up, he pulled out his revolver and pumped three bullets into Driggs. Then, laughing insanely, Rimbaud staggered back, still holding the canteen high.

"Ha . . . ha . . . ha, the strong will always kill the weak. I, Rimbaud, am strong. I . . . aiehh . . ."

The legionnaire crashed to the dry, hot sand. As he was backing up, his feet had caught in the dead man's shirt. He had stumbled! And, just beyond his clutching fingers, precious water was flowing out of an open canteen.

When Rimbaud finally picked up the canteen, it was empty. Already, black specks were circling in the sky. He could never make it back now. As the sun became hotter and the specks larger, Rimbaud felt his strength ebbing away. Through fogging eyes, he was just able to see the fallen figure of a man he had called weak . . . the man who was able to strike him down from the dead!

WEIRD WORLDS

WHAT IS A DIMENSION? IMAGINE THAT OUR WORLD IS A TUBE ONE FOOT LONG AND ONE INCH IN DIAMETER. WE LIVE IN THAT TUBE. HOWEVER, THERE MAY BE OTHER TUBES OF LIFE WHICH WE DO NOT KNOW ABOUT... WHICH WE CAN'T IMAGINE! THEY ARE THE... DIMENSIONS DANGER!

THE TWELFTH DIMENSION IS THE WORLD OF THE "JELLY HORROR!" HERE, UNSEEN BY OUR EYES, HUGE GLOBS OF ORANGE JELLY SLIDE BACK AND FORTH. THEY HAVE THE POWER TO SWALLOW UP AN ENTIRE CITY!

DIMENSION Z HAS LIFE SIMILAR TO OURS. WHEN OUR DIMENSION CAME TO BE, IT SOMEHOW SEPARATED FROM US. THE LIVING THINGS IN IT LOOK LIKE MEN BUT HAVE NO MINDS... JUST THE INSANE DESIRE TO KILL AND EAT EVERYTHING IN SIGHT...

HAVING NO BODIES, JUST SWIRLING RINGS OF ATOMS, THE "THING" OF DIMENSION INVISIBLE HAVE DEVELOPED SCREECHING VOICES. TO ENTER THEIR DIMENSION, ONE WOULD SEE NOTHING BUT HEAR SHRILL CRIES, SO POWERFUL AS TO CRACK OUR SKULLS LIKE EGGSHELLS!

IN DIMENSION 9, THERE EXIST SLIMY, CRAWLING MONSTERS WHO LIVE IN WATER. THEY LIVE IN THE CONSTANT MOISTURE OF OUR AIR AND MOVE ONLY WHEN WINDS FROM OUR ATMOSPHERE HIT THEM.

THIS IS AN EERIE STUDY IN GREED WOVEN AROUND THE MYSTERIOUS SKEIN OF "TIME"...TIME, THAT WHICH WE LIVE IN, DREAM IN, AND, DIE IN...AS DID STAN HARDEN, WHOSE GREED PUGHED HIM THROUGH TIME'S VEIL, INTO THE...

Monster's Maze

SAVE ME, *SAVE ME!* CAN'T YOU *HEAR ME!!* I'VE SLIPPED BACK IN TIME -- THE MONSTER IS AFTER ME --- HELP, *HELP!!*

EXCITEMENT FIRED THE BLOOD OF PROFESSOR STANLEY HARDEN AND HIS FRIENDS, EILEEN AND TOM WEBER. THEY HAD FOUND MYSTERIOUS HIDDEN TUNNELS BENEATH THE HISTORIC CRUST OF THE ISLAND OF CRETE...

MAGNIFICENT! *WHAT* IS THIS THAT WE'VE DISCOVERED, HARDEN?

I THINK I KNOW, WEBER. BUT IT'S FANTASTIC! UTTERLY FANTASTIC!

WHOA! WE'RE OUT OF ROPE! IF WE GO ON IN THIS MAZE WITHOUT IT, WE'LL NEVER FIND OUR WAY OUT AGAIN...

LOOK! A ROOM UP AHEAD!

COME ON! WE CAN GO THAT FAR WITHOUT THE ROPE!

THEY RUSHED INTO THE ROOM... AND ALSO INTO ONE OF THE STRANGEST ADVENTURES EVER EXPERIENCED BY HUMAN BEINGS...

RUBIES, DIAMONDS, GOLD! A FORTUNE, A FORTUNE!

AND THE WALL... LOOK AT THAT PAINTING!

OHH! HOW UGLY!

WE'VE STUMBLED INTO THE LABYRINTH! THE HOME OF THE MINOTAUR— A HALF MAN, HALF BULL MONSTER THAT LIVED THOUSANDS OF YEARS AGO! IT DEVOURED VICTIMS WHO WERE BROUGHT TO THIS MAZE OF TUNNELS AND LEFT HERE--- AS HUMAN SACRIFICES!

HOW UTTERLY FANTASTIC THAT WE... THREE AMERICAN TOURISTS---SHOULD HAVE FOUND THESE TUNNELS! TUNNELS NO ONE HAS SEEN FOR TWO THOUSAND YEARS OR MORE!

OH-OH! WE'VE GOT COMPANY! LOOK...

A SKELETON! OH, TOM!

HA-HA! DON'T BE FRIGHTENED, EILEEN! THAT CHAP WON'T HURT YOU!

HE'S BEEN DEAD ABOUT TWO THOUSAND YEARS, JUDGING FROM HIS BONES. BUT--- THE FUNNY THING IS-- HE'S WEARING A WRIST WATCH!

A WHAT? A WATCH!! THEN-- HE CAN'T HAVE BEEN DEAD FOR TWO THOUSAND YEARS!

FORGET IT---WHAT WE'VE GOT TO CONCENTRATE ON IS THIS FORTUNE WE'VE FOUND! JUST THINK OF IT-- A FORTUNE-!

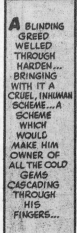

A BLINDING GREED WELLED THROUGH HARDEN... BRINGING WITH IT A CRUEL, INHUMAN SCHEME... A SCHEME WHICH WOULD MAKE HIM OWNER OF ALL THE COLD GEMS CASCADING THROUGH HIS FINGERS...

WE'VE NO WAY TO CARRY THIS OUT. YOU TWO WAIT HERE --I'LL GO OUT, GET THE BAGS, AND BE BACK WITHIN THE HOUR!

STAY HERE ALONE? OH, NO, PLEASE; I---

WE'LL BE SAFE, EILEEN. HARDEN'S RIGHT--SOMEBODY HAS TO GET SOMETHING TO CARRY IT OUT IN...

So Harden left Tom and Eileen and followed the rope trail down the mouldering maze of tunnels until, finally, he came to the hole through which they had first entered...

THEY'LL NEVER FIND THEIR WAY OUT WITH THIS ROPE GONE! BUT THE SECRET MARKS I'VE MADE ON THE TUNNEL WALLS WILL ENABLE ME TO FIND MY WAY BACK AFTER THEY'VE *STARVED* TO DEATH!

NOW TO CLIMB UP... ¿UFF¿... AND OUT... BLOCK UP THE HOLE... ¿UFF¿ AND WAIT FOR THEM TO STARVE-- ¿UFF¿ TO DEATH---

BUT THEN, SUDDENLY, WITHOUT WARNING...

ROOF'S FALLING IN AGAIN--- *AHHH--!*

HARDEN'S HEAD EXPLODED WITH PAIN WHEN HE STRUCK THE GROUND... THERE WAS A PECULIAR WHIRLING SENSATION AS HE PLUNGED INTO UNCONSCIOUSNESS. WHEN CONSCIOUSNESS RETURNED, HE GOT UP GROGGILY.

OHHH.... MY HEAD. BLASTED FALL KNOCKED ME OUT. OHHH.... WHAT A BUMP! I'VE GOT TO GET OUT OF HERE...WONDER IF THE ROPE IS STILL WHOLE...

SLOWLY HARDEN ROSE-- AND GOT THE SHOCK OF HIS LIFE! SOMETHING -- NO, *EVERYTHING* -- HAD CHANGED!

WHAT THE-- THE HOLE IS GONE! AND THE TUNNELS-- THE PAINTINGS --*THEY'RE LIKE NEW!* AND THERE'S NO MUSTY ODOR --*WHAT HAS HAPPENED*--

THEN, QUITE ABRUPTLY, HARDEN SENSED THE ASTOUNDING TRUTH. AND, WHO MOMENTS BEFORE HAD BEEN A COLD, CALCULATING MURDERER, SUDDENLY BECAME A FEVERISH, TERROR-RIDDEN HULK.

IT CAN'T BE--¿GASP¿--BUT-- IT IS, *IT IS!* IT'S ALL NEW! THAT BLOW SOMEHOW--HURLED ME BACK TWO THOUSAND YEARS IN TIME! I'VE--*I'VE GONE BACK TO THE AGE OF THE MINOTAUR-- THE MONSTER OF CRETE!!*

For a few terrible moments he crouched against the wall in a numbing frenzy of shock and terror... then he went temporarily insane with fear and disbelief -- and began to run blindly, wildly, screaming --

NO, NO! I'VE GONE MAD! HA-HA-HA--! I'M DREAMING! IT CAN'T BE-- IT CAN'T BE!! HELP-- HELP!! HA-HA-HA-HA--

ARGHH!

YAAAAAA--!

...THE MINOTAUR...

YAAAAAAAAA!

ARGHHH!

Harden was no longer a man, no longer "human"!... but an animal, a raving animal propelled by searing terror... he ran ... and ran ... and then --- mercifully -- unconsciousness broke over him again.

HELP--- A-HA-HA-HA--- HELP. A DEAD-END TUNNEL! NO, NO! AHHHH!

And as Harden fell, there were sounds beyond the tunnel's dead-end. Suddenly, a door opened... admitting three giant men...

QUICKLY! TAKE HIM IN. I WILL HOLD THE MONSTER BACK!

AYE--!

WHEN HARDEN OPENED HIS EYES HE SAW HE WAS NO LONGER IN THE LABYRINTH'S MAZE... BUT HIS TERROR REMAINED CONSTANT... FOR HE WAS STILL LOST IN THE DEPTHS OF TIME...

OH...MY HEAD--:GASP:--WHAT--WHERE AM I--WHO--WHO ARE YOU--

QUIET, ATHENIAN.

HOW YOU ENTERED THE MAZE, ATHENIAN, I KNOW NOT. YOU ARE NOT SCHEDULED TO GO THERE UNTIL TONIGHT. THUS WE SAVED YOU--- FOR TONIGHT!

TOM--EILEEN! IT'S YOU! LOOK-- IF IT'S A CONFESSION YOU WANT-- YES, YES! I TRIED TO KILL YOU! NOW STOP--PLEASE STOP THIS FANTASTIC TORTURE!! PLEASE--

KEEP YOUR PLACE, ATHENIAN! YOU DO NOT TOUCH THE RULERS OF CRETE!!

BUT--I'M AMERICAN! PLEASE-- :SOB: STOP THIS--THIS GAME! STOP! STOP! YOU CAN'T MAKE ME BELIEVE I'VE GONE BACK IN TIME A THOUSAND YEARS-- YOU CAN'T--:SOB:!!

THE MAN STILL RAVES!

NONETHELESS, HE GOES TO THE MAZE AGAIN... A SACRIFICE FOR THE MINOTAUR...

TOM--:SOB:---EILEEN--- WAIT---W-A-I-----T--- :SOB:---!

THE DOOR CLOSED WITH A HOLLOW BOOM....AND HARDEN WAS ALONE WITH HIS GIANT GUARD...

THEN IT'S TRUE. I'VE GOT TO FACE IT. SOMEHOW...I'VE SLIPPED BACK IN TIME....AND THOUGH THOSE TWO LOOK LIKE TOM AND EILEEN, THEY'RE NOT. I'VE GOT TO ESCAPE. BUT HOW CAN I GET BY THIS GIANT....IF ONLY I HAD A--A GUN!!

IN HIS TERROR HARDEN HAD FORGOTTEN THE WEAPON IN HIS KNAPSACK! FURIOUSLY, HE SEARCHED THROUGH IT, AND...

MY GUN! I'D FORGOTTEN IT! HA-HA-HA! NOW WE'LL SEE!

ONCE AGAIN HARDEN'S EYES HELD A MURDERER'S GLINT. HE STRODE ACROSS THE TEMPLE ROOM UNTIL THE GIANT GUARD SPOKE OMINOUSLY..

BACK, ATHENIAN! COME NO CLOSER!

OKAY, GARGANTUA! THIS IS CLOSE ENOUGH FOR MY LITTLE SURPRISE... STRAIGHT OUT OF THE 20TH CENTURY!

ARRR---

HA-HA-HA-HA-HA--

BANG! BANG! BANG!

THE BULLETS' IMPACT ROCKED THE GIANT, BUT DID NOT FELL HIM. HE STAGGERED FORWARD AND HARDEN, CRINGING BACK IN TERROR, EMPTIED THE REVOLVER--

ATHENIAN-- YOU-- AHH-- YOU --DIE NOW!

FALL, I SAY, FALL, FALL--!

BANG! BANG! BANG!

CLICK CLICK! CLICK!

CRASHHH

FALL-- FALL-- HA-HA-HA-HA--!!

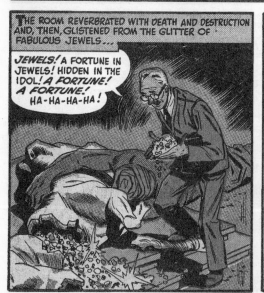

THE ROOM REVERBERATED WITH DEATH AND DESTRUCTION AND, THEN, GLISTENED FROM THE GLITTER OF FABULOUS JEWELS...

JEWELS! A FORTUNE IN JEWELS! HIDDEN IN THE IDOL! A FORTUNE! A FORTUNE! HA-HA-HA-HA!

DESPERATE AS HE WAS TO ESCAPE, HARDEN STILL PAUSED AND GREEDILY SCOOPED POUND AFTER POUND OF JEWELS INTO A CHEST HE FOUND NEARBY. THEN HE LEFT...BUT WITH ONE THOUGHT HAMMERING IN HIS BRAIN...

PUFF!--GOT TO FIGURE A WAY TO GET BACK TO THE 20TH CENTURY! THERE MUST BE A WAY--PUFF!--THERE MUST BE---

SUDDENLY, HARDEN'S FRANTIC EYES SAW A DOOR CLEVERLY HIDDEN IN A STEEP HILLSIDE. HE HURRIED TOWARDS IT, OPENED IT, AND ENTERED...

THERE--¿PUFF¿--I'LL HIDE IN HERE---- AND FIGURE OUT A WAY TO GET BACK TO MY CENTURY--¿PUFF¿ I'LL HAVE *TWO* FORTUNES IN JEWELS---*TWO!!*

AS HARDEN TOOK IN HIS SURROUNDINGS HE ALSO TOOK IN HORROR -- COMPLETE, OVERWHELMING HORROR! THE ROOM WAS FAMILIAR!

NOW, I--OH--NO, *NO!* THAT PICTURE--- THE TUNNEL ENTRANCES-- IT'S THE *SAME ROOM WE FOUND IN THE 20TH CENTURY!!* I'M IN THE SAME ROOM! IT'S THE *ENTRANCE TO THE MONSTER'S MAZE!!*

GOT TO GET OUT---*AHH, NO!*-- THE DOOR---THERE'S NO HANDLE---*THERE'S NO HANDLE---NO--NO--!!*

AND THEN HARDEN HEARD A SOUND THAT TURNED HIS VERY SOUL TO ICE! A LOW GROWL....A SAVAGE, THROATY, HIDEOUS CRY....

ARRRR-- EEEE----R-R-R-R-R

THE MINOTAUR! *HELP! HELP! HELP...*

AND IN THE LAST, TERRIBLE, SCREAMING SECONDS OF HIS LIFE HARDEN REALIZED THREE THINGS. THE FIRST WAS THE SIGNIFICANCE OF THE WRIST WATCH....

A SKELETON! OH, TOM!

HA-HA! DON'T BE FRIGHTENED, EILEEN! *THAT* CHAP WON'T HURT YOU.

HE'S BEEN DEAD ABOUT TWO THOUSAND YEARS, JUDGING FROM HIS BONES! BUT-- THE FUNNY THING IS---HE'S WEARING A WRIST WATCH!!

THE SECOND WAS THE CRUSHING KNOWLEDGE THAT THE WEBERS HAD SOMEHOW ES-CAPED AFTER HE'D ABANDONED THEM IN THE 20TH CENTURY! FOR, IF THEY HAD NOT, THEN THERE WOULD HAVE BEEN *THREE* SKELETONS IN THE ROOM! THE THIRD REALIZATION WAS ECHOED IN HARDEN'S LAST HOARSE SCREAM....

THAT WAS *MY* WATCH ON THAT SKELETON---*THAT WAS MY SKELETON--AHHHHH!!*

THE END

SCIENTIFIC ODDITIES

SUN SPOTS (GREAT ELECTRICAL STORMS) TRAVEL ACROSS THE FACE OF THE SUN IN CYCLES. RUNNING IN HARMONY WITH THESE SUN SPOT CYCLES ARE WARS, REVOLUTIONS AND OTHER SOCIAL UPHEAVALS. COINCIDENCE?

1951

1928 TODAY IT RAINED CONSTANTLY.

A FOREMOST SCIENTIST FOUND THAT WEATHER CONDITIONS HAVE A TENDENCY TO REPEAT EVERY 23 YEARS!

PEOPLE ALSO HAVE THEIR CYCLES. THERE ARE TIMES WHEN THE PERSON FEELS HAPPY AND AT PEACE WITH THE WORLD AND THERE ARE TIMES WHEN THAT SAME PERSON FEELS THE DAY OF DOOM HAS COME!

THE WORLD'S GREATEST BLAST DID NOT TAKE PLACE IN JAPAN. ON AUGUST 27, 1883, UNDER THE ISLAND OF KARRATOA NEAR JAVA, A BLAST OCCURRED WHICH KILLED 35,000 PEOPLE, DARKENED THE SUN THE WORLD OVER WITH FLYING DEBRIS AND CREATED A TIDAL WAVE OF 100 FEET.

AUGUST 1

AUGUST 15

IF THE MOON SUDDENLY EXPLODED, WE WOULD SEE THE FLASH IN A LITTLE OVER A SECOND. BUT WE WOULD HEAR THE EXPLOSION ABOUT 14 DAYS LATER.

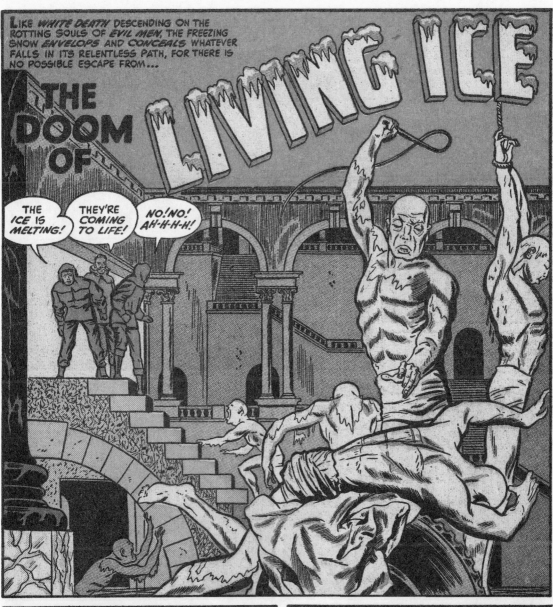

Like *WHITE DEATH* descending on the rotting souls of *EVIL MEN,* the freezing snow *ENVELOPS* and *CONCEALS* whatever falls in its relentless path, for there is no possible escape from...

THE DOOM OF LIVING ICE

THE *ICE* IS *MELTING!*

THEY'RE COMING TO LIFE!

NO! NO! AH-H-H-H!

In the *FROZEN, BARREN* wastes of the vast and *STRANGELY SILENT* north, three explorers move blindly through a *VICIOUS* storm...

I CAN'T SEE A *THING!*

WE'D BETTER FIND *SHELTER* SOON!!

THE WIND IS SO *COLD* IT SEEMS TO BE *EATING* INTO MY *FLESH!!!*

WE'D BETTER GO INTO THIS *CAVE* FOR THE NIGHT!

IT CERTAINLY LOOKS *BIG* ENOUGH! AT LEAST WE'LL BE *SAFE!*

THE THREE MEN WALK THROUGH THE *HUGE* AND *PITCH-BLACK* CAVE GLAD TO BE FREE OF THE STORM. THEN, OUT OF THE DARKNESS...

LOOK! AN *ANCIENT TEMPLE!*

WHAT A *STRANGE* THING TO FIND IN THE MIDDLE OF A *CAVE!*

THERE ARE MEN HERE!! ANCIENT, MONSTROUS MEN!!!

AND THEY'RE ALL *ENCASED* IN *ICE!!!*

WHAT IS IT THEY'RE *DOING?* LET'S GET UP CLOSER! WE'VE *DISCOVERED* SOMETHING!

LOOK! THIS MAN IS BEING *TORTURED* ON THE *RACK!*

WHAT A *GHASTLY* SMILE THERE IS ON THE OTHER'S FACE! THE ICE HAS PRESERVED EVERYTHING!

THIS MUST BE SOME SORT OF *ANCIENT TORTURE CHAMBER!*

THE ROOF MUST HAVE *CAVED* IN THOUSANDS OF YEARS AGO AND *BURIED THEM ALL!*

THE *TORTURED* AND THE *TORTURERS--* BURIED TOGETHER!

THEY'RE *ALL* ENCASED IN *ICE!* THE AIR IS SO COLD HERE THEY MUST HAVE *FROZEN* IN THE POSITIONS IN WHICH THEY *DIED!!*

WHAT A *REPULSIVE* WAY TO DIE!! THEY'RE *HELD FAST* IN AN ICY TRAP FOR- EVER!!!

SUDDENLY, A *STRANGE* IDEA IS FORMED IN AN *ACTIVE, SCIENTIFIC* MIND... AND THE *FROSTY WIND* THAT *WHIRS* THROUGH THE CAVE LIKE AN INVISIBLE DEMON BECOMES *SHARPER...* AND *COLDER...*

SAY, WHY DON'T WE LIGHT A *TREMENDOUS FIRE* IN THE TEMPLE... AND *MELT* THE ICE THAT SURROUNDS THESE CREATURES?

WE COULD BRING SPECIMENS BACK TO OUR LABORATORY AND FIND OUT WHAT *CIVILIZATION* THEY REPRESENT!!

WE'LL BUILD THE FIRE *NOW!*

I HAVE THE *MATCHES!*

THIS SHOULD BE THE *GREATEST* EXPERIMENT OF ALL TIME!

THIS SHOULD DO IT!!

SOME OF THE ICE IS MELTING *ALREADY!*

IT WON'T BE LONG *NOW!*

As THE FIRE *LEAPS* ABOUT THE *GHASTLY FROZEN* FIGURES, THE ICE THAT ENCASES THEM BEGINS TO *MELT* QUICKLY... AND THE *LOATHSOME* CREATIONS OF ANOTHER DAY BEGIN TO *MOVE*...TO *STIR*...TO *RETURN TO LIFE!*....

ERGH-H-H-H!!!

AARR-R-R-HHH!!

THEY'RE *LIVING AGAIN!!*

HE SEEMS TO BE *SMILING!*--AS IF HE'S BEEN RELEASED FROM *UNBEARABLE AGONY* AND *BONDAGE!*

AWWGH-H-H-H!

UTTERING *WILD, UNEARTHLY SOUNDS,* THE DREADFUL BEINGS, FREE FROM THEIR *LIVING DEATH,* TURN ON THEIR TORMENTORS TO DRAG THEM TO THE *DOOM THEY* HAD SUFFERED.!!....

WE'D BETTER STAY BEHIND THESE STAIRS!! THIS IS *AMAZING!*

IT'S TOO HORRIBLE!! I CAN'T LOOK!!

THEY'RE *TURNING* ON THE MEN WHO TORTURED THEM!!

AAIIEEE-E-E-E!!!

I CAN'T STAND THIS ANY MORE! LET ME OUT! LET ME OUT!!!

BE QUIET, YOU *FOOL!!!*

THEY'VE SEEN US! WHAT SHALL WE DO?

LET'S RUN FOR IT!!

HURRY! HURRY!!

THEIR *PRIMITIVE FURY* AROUSED BY THE *INTRUDERS* OF THEIR *SACRED* VAULT OF *TORTURE* AND *TERROR,* THE *FOUL* CREATURES MOVE TOWARDS THEIR *HUMAN PREY* WITH *ANIMAL LUST...*

EIRRRGG-H-H-H!

IF WE CAN GET OUT OF THE *CAVE* WE'LL BE SAFE!!

THEY'RE COMING AFTER US!!!

THEY'RE GETTING *CLOSER!* HOW CAN THEY MOVE SO *FAST?*

BUT WHAT'S *HAPPENING* TO THEM? THEY LOOK AS IF THEY'RE *DECOMPOSING!*

*A*NCIENT BODIES DWINDLE SUDDENLY INTO *FETID* MASSES OF *DECAYED FLESH...FESTERING* FACES, ARMS, LEGS, CRUMBLE TO NOTHING BUT *GHASTLY, GREEN DUST!!!*

THEY'VE BEEN *PETRIFIED* IN THAT *ICE TOO LONG!!* THEY COULDN'T TAKE THE AIR ANY MORE!

THE ENTRANCE ISN'T MUCH FURTHER!! HURRY!!!

THEY GOT HARRIS!

GR-R-RAUGH-H!

NO! N--- AHH-H-H!!

THE ANCIENT ROCKS OF THE CAVE CAN HOLD *NO LONGER*, AND *RELENTLESSLY* THEY RAIN UPON THE HEADS OF THE *TERRIFIED* MEN!

LOOK OUT! THE ROOF IS CAVING IN!!

WE CAN'T GET OUT!!!

CRACK

CRUMBLE

BOOM

THE ENTRANCE IS BLOCKED! WE'RE TRAPPED!!

PULL AT THE ROCKS!!

THERE'S ONE OF THOSE--- *MONSTERS!!* HE SEEMS TO BE BECKONING TO US!

MAYBE HE WANTS TO HELP US!

THERE'S HARRIS! HE'S--UGHH-H-H!!

LOOK AT HIS BODY!!

AS THE MEN GAZE UPON THE BLOOD-SOAKED CORPSE OF THEIR FRIEND, A *SUDDEN CHILL* COMES INTO THE AIR, *COLD* AND *FRIGHTENING* LIKE THE *PALE, MOIST HAND* OF DEATH!!

H-H-HIS BODY!! IT'S BEING COVERED WITH-- ICE!!

IT'S AS IF THEY *NEVER EXISTED!* WE FREED THEM FROM THE *DOOM* OF *LIVING ICE*--BUT *ONLY* TO DECOMPOSE WHEN THE AIR HIT THEM.

WE MUST GET OUT OF HERE!!

MAYBE IF WE DIG *LONG ENOUGH* WE'LL FIND OUR WAY OUT!!

WE MUST! I DON'T WANT TO MEET *HARRIS'* FATE!!!

WITHOUT WARNING, THE SAME *DEADLY CHILL* ENVELOPS THE CAVE... THE SAME *ICY FOREBODING* OF *TERRIBLE DOOM*...

M-M-MY HAND!! IT'S COATED WITH-- ICE!!

MY FACE!! IT'S ALSO COVERED WITH *ICE!*

WE'RE *DOOMED* TO DIE HERE--- LIKE *HARRIS* AND THE *OTHERS!* *DOOMED* FOR A *LIVING DEATH* IN ICE-- UNTIL WE ARE *FREED!!!*

WE WILL *NEVER* BE *FREED* FROM THE *DOOM* OF *LIVING ICE!!*

WE ARE *DOOMED! DOOMED! D-O-O-M-E-D!!*

...AND OUTSIDE THE *BLACK HORROR* OF THE CAVE, IN THE *WHITE* FURY OF A RAGING STORM, TWO SEARCHERS APPROACH TO CURIOUSLY LOOK UPON THE WALL OF STONE THAT ADMITS *NOBODY* TO ITS *SINISTER SECRETS*...

FUNNY, BUT I DON'T REMEMBER THIS OLD CAVE BEING *WALLED UP* BEFORE!

YEAH - WELL, THEY *COULDN'T* BE IN *THERE!* LET'S PUSH ON... IT'S GETTING AWFULLY COLD!!

THE END.

CHAMBER OF CHILLS

TALES OF TERROR AND SUSPENSE

CHAMBER OF CHILLS

MAGAZINE

PDC
No.
24
DEC.

10c

WE DARE YOU....
TO OPEN THE MYSTERIOUS DOOR INTO A WORLD OF HORROR!

FORMULA 2013
MOLECULAR REDUCTION SOLUTION

Miss Lee-Fashions

Style #633 MISTY LACE
Imported Chantilly Lace

Sheer enchantment with the magic of lace! . . . Exquisitely lovely sheer net clings lovingly over bared shoulders to a figure-caressing bodice of imported Chantilly Lace that falls into a graceful peplum, and cascades helplessly to the hemline of the widest "of wide, filmy dancing skirts (over its own slip). Colorful blushing flowers highlight a tiny waist. In Superb Quality Celanese Taffeta and Marquisette net

BEWITCHING COLORS:
- BLACK
- PEACOCK
- AMERICAN BEAUTY
- WHITE
- ROSE

IN ALL SIZES
9-11-13-15-17
10-12-14-16-18-20

only **9**⁹⁸

16½-18½-20½
22½-24½-26½
38-40-42-44-46-48

only **10**⁹⁸

Style #C-8—POLKA DOTS

For dancing . . . for romancing . . . Lace the "Gretchen" bodice firmly to the breathtaking polka dot decolletage. The full-bodied skirt swishes and rustles as you walk, as you dance. In finest quality silky rayon.

IN BEAUTIFUL COLORS:
- BLACK
- BROWN
- GREEN
- AMERICAN BEAUTY

IN ALL SIZES only 6⁹⁸
9-11-13-15-17
10-12-14-16-18-20

16½-18½-20½ only **7**⁹⁸
22½-24½-26½
38-40-42-44-46-48

Send 10¢ for our latest catalog!

CHAMBER OF CHILLS MAGAZINE, DECEMBER, 1951, Vol. 1, No. 24, IS PUBLISHED EVERY OTHER MONTH by WITCHES TALES, INC., 1860 Broadway, New York 23, N.Y. Application for second class entry pending at the Post Office at New York, N.Y under the Act of March 3, 1879. Single copies 10c. Subscription rates, 10 issues for $1.00 in the U.S. and possessions, elsewhere $1.50. All names in this periodical are entirely fictitious and no identification with actual persons is intended. Contents copyrighted, 1951, by Witches Tales, Inc., New York City.

Printed in the U.S.A.

WON'T YOU COME IN?

Draw back the iron door knocker, dear reader. Let it fall twice. Be ready to enter the *CHAMBER OF CHILLS* again!

What is in store for you in the chamber? What mystery lurks behind the door? Use this message as a key and find out!

First, twist the key a little.

That's right! Ah, already the door opens a bit and there can be seen *THE LOST SOULS!* Read this story of another world and what happens when a mortal dares to invade the "forbidden land!"

Now, turn the key some more. Look! *THE PALE LIGHT OF DEATH* streams through the widened crack. Yes, dear reader, this account of terror will show you how powerful the revenge of GHOSTS can be!

Go ahead, turn the key! Ah, you cringe back. You see two men sprawled grotesquely on the ground. What happened to them? Read *TWO WAYS TO DIE!*

You also see a book, don't you? The story about it is weird and unbelievable. Yet three people died because of it! It is the *BOOK OF VENGEANCE!*

Now, turn the key all the way! Enter and see fully the horror of the

CHAMBER OF CHILLS

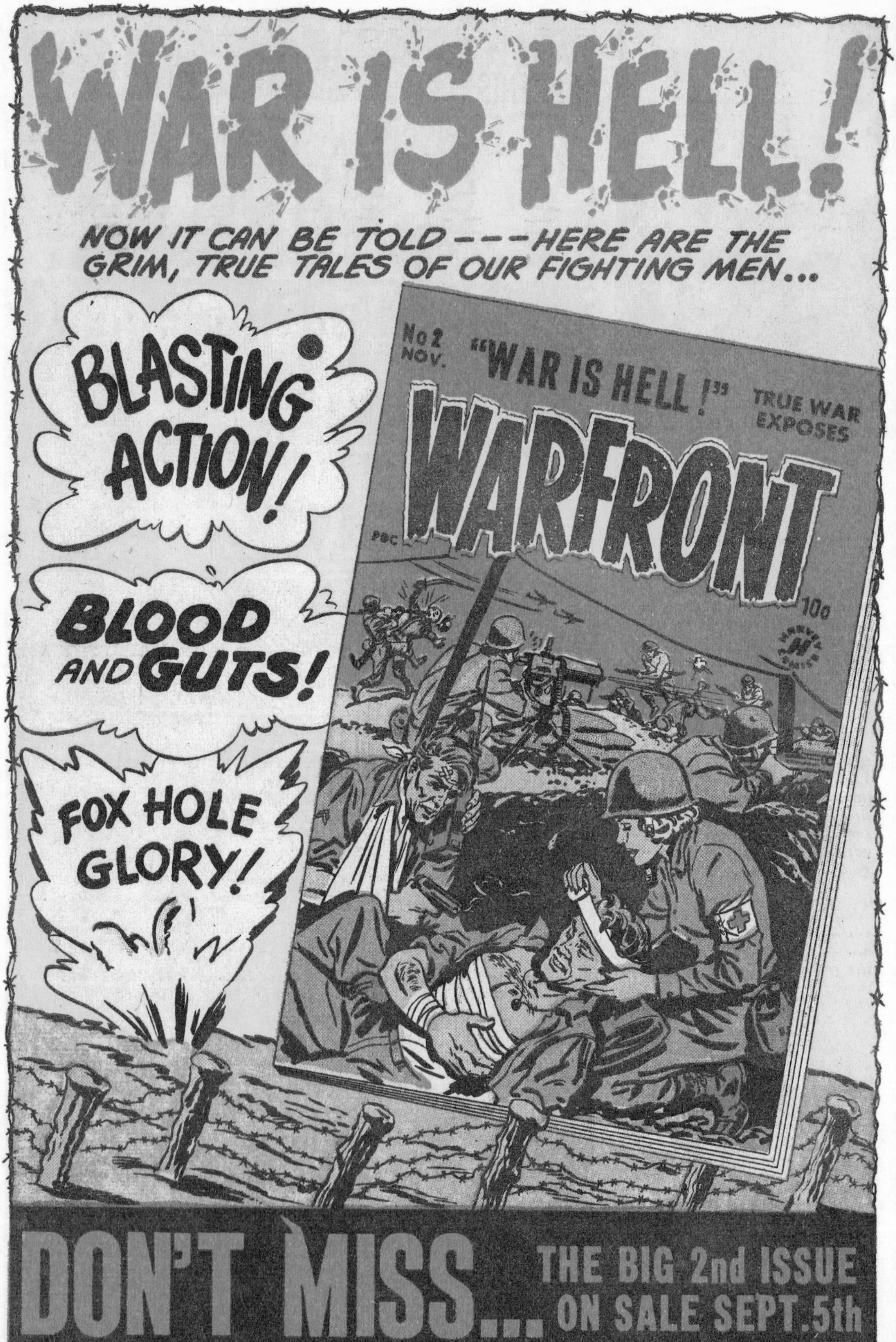

WAR IS HELL!
NOW IT CAN BE TOLD---HERE ARE THE GRIM, TRUE TALES OF OUR FIGHTING MEN...
BLASTING ACTION!
BLOOD AND GUTS!
FOX HOLE GLORY!
No 2 NOV.
"WAR IS HELL!"
TRUE WAR EXPOSES
WARFRONT
10¢
DON'T MISS...
THE BIG 2nd ISSUE ON SALE SEPT. 5th

IN THE STEAMING, *CRAWLING DARKNESS* OF THE FLORIDA SWAMP COUNTRY, THE GHASTLY *SPECTERS OF HORROR* PLAN A MURDER...SHOWING THAT THERE ARE...

TWO WAYS TO DIE!

JAMES, THERE'S NO WAY OUT...OUR MONEY IS *GONE!* WE *MUST* DO SOMETHING TO GET MONEY! I'D EVEN *KILL* FOR IT!..

I'VE BEEN THINKING, LESLIE! *OLD AUNT LENORE* IS OUR *ONLY LIVING RELATIVE*... AND SHE'S *VERY RICH!* SUPPOSE WE *LURED* HER DOWN HERE...!

JAMES, ARE YOU THINKING THE *SAME THING* I AM...?

EXACTLY! GET HER DOWN HERE- AND IF ANYTHING *WERE TO HAPPEN* TO HER... AS HER ONLY RELATIVES, WE'D GET HER MONEY!!

THE DREADFUL *THOUGHT* OF *MURDER* WAS PUT INTO ACTION! AN INVITATION WAS SENT AND ACCEPTED, AND FROM A *DISTANT, NORTHERN* PLACE CAME... AUNT LENORE!

DEAR AUNT LENORE...YOU DON'T KNOW HOW JAMES AND I HAVE BEEN *LOOKING FORWARD* TO...SEEING YOU HERE!

THIS IS YOUR ROOM, AUNTIE! IT'S NOT THE CLEANEST PLACE... BUT WE HOPE YOU WILL ENJOY IT...FOR *AS LONG AS YOU STAY*...!

IT'S...LOVELY! THANK YOU, NEPHEWS...NOW PLEASE EXCUSE ME! I MUST- *PREPARE SOME THINGS!*

THOSE *FOOLS!* LITTLE DO THEY KNOW WHAT THEIR AUNT LENORE IS...HOW I HAVE MASTERED THE *BLACK ARTS! HEE! HEE!* I KNOW WHAT THEY WANT TO DO!

SPIRITS OF THE SHADOW...HEAR ME! I, YOUR *SISTER OF DARKNESS*, CALL YOU! PHANTOMS OF EVIL, ARISE TO DO BATTLE AGAINST MY NEPHEWS!

I SEE YOU, *MESSENGER OF DEATH!* YOU ANSWER MY CALL! WE WILL KILL... KILL THOSE WHO WOULD KILL ME!

I'M ALL FOR *DROWNING* HER...RIGHT *HERE* IN THIS POOL!

NO, YOU FOOL! WE CAN FORGE A *SUICIDE* NOTE FOR HER...AND *HANG* HER! WAIT- I HAVE A *BETTER* IDEA....!

JAMES PLACED A METRONOME OUTSIDE LENORE'S WINDOW... HOPING THAT THE TIP-TAP OF THE MACHINE WOULD DRIVE LENORE *INSANE... IN THE NIGHT!*

SHE'LL THINK SOME *SWAMP FIEND* IS TAPPING ON HER WINDOW! WHA- I THOUGHT I HEARD THE OLD FOOL *LAUGHING...*

HEE! HEE! HEE!

IT'S YOUR *IMAGINATION!* I STILL THINK WE OUGHT TO *DROWN* HER!

ALONE IN THEIR ROOM, IN THE DEAD OF NIGHT, JAMES AND LESLIE LISTENED FOR THE *WEIRD, TAPPING SOUND...*

I CAN HEAR IT... IT SOUNDS SO *STRANGE...*

YES... IT SEEMS TOO *NEAR...* TOO *LOUD...*

TAP-TAP TAP-TAP

LESLIE... IT'S LOUDER... IT SEEMS TO BE COMING FROM *THIS ROOM!*

TAP-TAP TAP-TAP

NO! NO! EEEYAHHH! LOOK! J-J-JAMES... L-LOOK!

THE WINDOW- LOOK- LOOK AT THE *WINDOW!* THE-THE TAPPING WAS HERE... IT'S COMING IN - *IN HERE!*

TAP-TAP TAP-TAP TAP-TAP!

EEEEEYYAAARRRGHGH!

TAP-TAP TAP-TAP!

BUT THE BRIGHTNESS OF THE NEXT MORNING CONVINCED THE MURDEROUS BROTHERS THAT THE TAPPING HAD ALL BEEN A *NIGHTMARE*...

OHHH, THAT *SPECTRAL HAND*...HORRIBLE! IT ALL SEEMS SO... *REAL!*

I KNEW WE SHOULD HAVE HUNG HER AND HAD IT OVER WITH! QUIET NOW... HERE SHE COMES!

GOOD MORNING, AUNTIE! I HOPE YOU... SLEPT WELL!

GRACIOUS, YES. *HEE! HEE!* IF YOU'LL EXCUSE ME, I'D LIKE TO WALK AROUND THE GROUNDS BEFORE BREAKFAST!

SHE—SHE DIDN'T HEAR A SOUND?? WE MUST GET RID OF HER AT ONCE! *DROWN HER!* THE STRAIN IS BEGINNING TO *GET ME!*

WAIT! I HAVE ONE MORE IDEA FOR DRIVING HER *MAD*... IF THAT FAILS, WE CAN HANG HER OR DROWN HER...

WE'LL PAINT THIS ON HER CEILING IN *PHOSPHORESCENT* PAINT! SHE WON'T BE ABLE TO SEE IT IN THE DAYTIME, BUT AT NIGHT... IT WILL *GLOW*...!

LET ME KNOW AS SOON AS YOU SEE HER COMING! BRRRR! THIS *HORRIBLE FACE* GIVES ME THE CREEPS... IT'S ALMOST ALIVE... *WATCHING!*

STRANGE... I, TOO, SEEM TO FEEL *SOMETHING WATCHING*... LET'S GET THIS OVER WITH!

FINISHED! IF THAT HORRIBLE FACE DOESN'T DRIVE HER CRAZY... WE'LL TAKE CARE OF HER IN THE OTHER WAYS...

NOW LET'S GET OUT OF HERE! SHE DIDN'T *SEE* US... *THERE'S NO WAY* FOR HER TO FIND OUT WE WERE *EVER* HERE!

PLANNING TO REMOVE THE *HIDEOUS CORPSE* THE NEXT DAY, THE BROTHERS WENT TO *BED!* AND AS *MIDNIGHT* CALLED TO THE CREATURES OF THE GRAVE, THE RIPPLING POOL WAS...

...AS GRISLY AS A...*RISING CORPSE!*

HEEEE! HEE! HEE! I FOOLED THEM! THEY DON'T KNOW THAT YOU CAN'T DROWN *THE DEAD!!* HEEE! HEE!

LESSSSLIEEE...JAAAMMESSSS...I AM COOOMMINGGGG...

LESLIE... *LISTEN...!*

WHA—WHAT *IS* IT...?

OHHHHHH...

NO! NO! WHATEVER YOU ARE...*DON'T COME ANY NEARER!!!*

MAD WITH *TERROR* AS THEY WATCHED THE *MONSTROUS THING* IN FRONT OF THEM, LESLIE AND JAMES DID NOT SEE THE *GHOSTLY HANDS* THAT SILENTLY *OPENED* THE WINDOW BEHIND THEM...

ARGRGR...NOWWWW... YOU MUST *DIE...!*

NO! NO! STAY *AWAY FROM US!*

THE LOST SOULS!

THE STRANGER WAS TIRED—ALL HE WANTED WAS TO SLEEP! HOW COULD HE KNOW HE WOULD WAKE UP AND MEET...

YEAAA! THE CITY OF THE DEAD—IT'S C-COMING ALIVE!!

C-CAN'T GO ON...REST... GOT TO REST...SLEEP... HERE..! OHH..!

W..? I FELL ASLEEP.. FUNNY! DARK...SO DARK...QUIET! W., WHERE IS EVERYBODY? WHERE!

THE END.

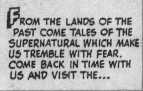

FROM THE LANDS OF THE PAST COME TALES OF THE SUPERNATURAL WHICH MAKE US TREMBLE WITH FEAR. COME BACK IN TIME WITH US AND VISIT THE...

Ancient Lands of Mystery!

IT IS BELIEVED THAT FROM *ASSYRIA* SPRUNG THE STORIES OF GHOSTS WHO WERE UNABLE TO SLEEP IN THEIR GRAVES. THESE MONSTERS ROAMED THE EARTH WAILING THEIR TORTURED CRIES. THE ASSYRIANS HAD SPECIAL MAGICAL RITES TO GUARD THEMSELVES AGAINST THESE RESTLESS DEMONS.

EGYPT IS CONSIDERED THE WELL OF WIZARDRY. FROM THAT LAND, ANCIENT AND MYSTERIOUS, HAVE COME THE FEARFUL SPELLS WHICH ARE SUPPOSED TO PLAGUE US TO THIS VERY DAY.

OUT OF THE COUNTRIES WHICH NOW FORM *CENTRAL EUROPE* HAS COME A MONSTER WHICH HAS NO EQUAL... *THE WEREWOLF!* THIS HIDEOUS CREATION HAS BEEN STORIED FOR CENTURIES AND ITS EVIL DEEDS WILL NEVER BE FORGOTTEN.

THE ORIGIN OF PHANTOMS IS TRACED TO ANCIENT *GREECE.* THE LITERATURE OF THAT LAND IS FULL OF GHOST SCENES AND ETERNAL DARKNESS IN WHICH DWELL WITCHES, PHANTOMS AND GHOULS!

THE PERFECT CRIME

"I committed the perfect crime. Ha ... ha, the perfect crime!"

The man continued to speak. From his appearance, it could be easily seen that he was accustomed to the finer things. The silence of the room tended to emphasize the words spoken by the man.

"Yes, those fools ... here I sit, the only man in history who has committed the perfect crime. I have murdered and no one will ever know who did it."

The daylight flooding into the room mellowed into the dusky grey of twilight.

"Everything is complete," continued the man. "Now I shall have the fame I've always wanted. When I die, the world will read what I have written and understand that I ... I ... have committed the perfect crime .. eh, yes?"

Another man had come into the room.

"Here is the food that you ordered. Will that be all?"

"All? Yes, yes, plenty. You may go."

Again the man was alone.

The twilight melted away into coal-black shafts of night. Hours passed. Once more a man entered.

"Are you sure you have no other desires?"

"No, you may leave. Oh, wait! Tell them I will be ready in a few minutes. I must look my best for my triumphal hour."

The minutes sped by. Three men, one dressed in black, entered the man's room. With the man walking boldly in the front, the four of them left the room and began to walk down a long corridor. On the side, two guards conversed softly ...

"There he goes, Lou, the guy who tried to commit the perfect crime."

"Yeah, he would of gotten away with it if he hadn't accidentally dropped his watch by the body of his wife."

"And he still thinks he committed the perfect crime. His mind snapped when the police told him about the watch. Well, they've gone in now. He'll get it any minute!"

WEIRD

MANY THINGS HAPPEN ON THIS EARTH WHICH ARE UNEXPLAINABLE. A SANE PERSON COULDN'T BELIEVE IN SUCH OCCURRENCES— —YET HE IS FORCED TO! ALL OF THESE MYSTERIOUS FACTS ARE BACKED BY FACT!

IN THE 18TH CENTURY AN ITALIAN POET DISCOVERED THAT A BOOK HE HAD WRITTEN FOR THE POPE CONTAINED A TYPOGRAPHICAL ERROR... THE SHOCK WAS SO GREAT THAT THE WRITER DROPPED DEAD!

DURING SIEGE OF DELHI, ALA-UD-DIN RAN OUT OF STONES FOR HIS CATAPULTS. REALIZING THAT HE NEEDED THE CATAPULTS FOR VICTORY, HE ORDERED BAGS OF GOLD TO BE USED FOR AMMUNITION!

FACTS

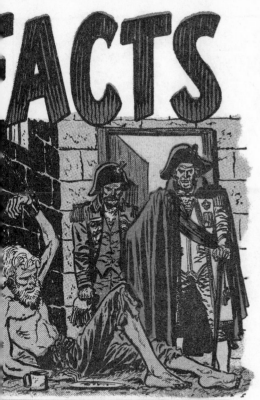

ECAUSE HE RIDICULED THE BALD KING LOUIS XIV
FRANCE, FRANCIS SELDON WAS CONFINED TO
E BASTILLE FOR 69 YEARS. HE SERVED HIS
L TERM AND LEFT PRISON A BROKEN, FOR-
TTEN MAN.

OOOOHH!
IEEEEH!!
ARRGH!

1801, THE BRITISH ATTEMPTED TO MOVE
GREEK TEMPLE FROM ATHENS TO ENGLAND.
WEVER, AS THE WORKMEN BEGAN TO TAKE
STONES APART, THE STATUES SUPPORT-
THE BUILDING BEGAN TO SHRIEK! NO
PLANATION WAS FOUND AND THE TEMPLE
WAS NEVER MOVED!

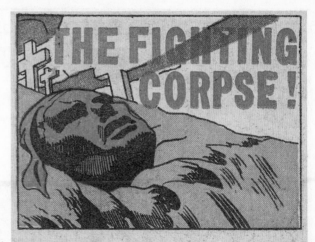

THE FIGHTING CORPSE !

"It's no use, Major! The men won't fight now that the General is dead!"

"But, Sergeant, they must fight. If they don't, the enemy will marshal its forces, attack and massacre our people."

"I realize that, sir, but without the General leading them, our soldiers are frightened to fight. If only the General could lead them, they. . . ."

"Wait, Sergeant, that's it!"

"What, sir?"

"We can have the General lead our men."

"But, Major, the General lies dead in his tent, a musket ball shattering his chest."

"I know, I know, but what if we were to prop his corpse up on his horse and announce to the men that their leader lives!"

"I . . . I . . . ."

"Sergeant, get four men you can trust and be at my tent in ten minutes!"

A half hour later, five men were dressing a bloody corpse! Nearby, a huge white stallion nervously stamped its feet as it saw the burden it would have to carry.

"Very good, Sergeant. Now, put the General on the horse. I will go and tell the men their leader lives."

When the battle began, the General's men took heart at the sight of their commander riding at their head. With shouts of joy and renewed courage, they charged into the ranks of the surprised enemy and fought like lions. In a short time their bugler was blowing full victory.

"Well, Sergeant," grinned the Major, "our little trick worked. Our men fought nicely with a 'dead' general."

"S-sir, I-I tried to reach you before. I-I don't know how to say this but I don't know what or who led the charge. You see, the horse bolted with the corpse BEFORE the battle began and only now has it been found in a pasture miles away!"

THE PALE LIGHT OF... DEATH!

IN THE FEARFUL HOURS BETWEEN BLACK MIDNIGHT AND GREY DAWN A STRANGE GLOW BATHES EVERYTHING— IT IS A PENETRATING GLOW— A DEADLY GLOW BECAUSE IT IS--

DANCE, DANCE ABOUT HIM IN THE WHITE LIGHT OF THE MOON!!

YOU MUST PAY THE PRICE OF EVIL!

LEAVE ME ALONE! HAVEN'T YOU TORTURED ME ENOUGH?

IN A DOCTOR'S OFFICE, A MAN RECEIVES PROFESSIONAL ADVICE WHICH, UNWITTINGLY, STARTS HIM DOWN THE DARK AND ENDLESS PATH OF FEAR AND EVIL!!

I STRONGLY RECOMMEND A VACATION IN THE COUNTRY, STEVE! YOUR NERVES ARE REALLY ACTING UP!

WHATEVER YOU SAY, DOC!

THE DOCTOR WAS RIGHT! THIS COUNTRY AIR CERTAINLY MAKES ME FEEL GOOD— LOOKS LIKE SOMEONE COMING DOWN THE ROAD!

IT MUST HAVE BEEN MY *IMAGINATION* OR A TRICK OF THE MOONLIGHT!

THE DAY OF THE WEDDING ARRIVES — AND INSTEAD OF JOYOUS LAUGHTER AND GAIETY THERE ARE LOW *MURMURS*, MOCKING LOOKS AND *GRIM, UNSPOKEN* FEARS!

SHE'S AN *HOUR* LATE! I WONDER WHAT'S HAPPENED TO HER!!

LOOKS LIKE THE BRIDE-TO-BE HAS VANISHED INTO THIN AIR!

HA HA! HA HO HO HO HO! SHE'S *GONE*!! SHE'S LEFT ME HERE LIKE A *FOOL* FOR THEM TO LAUGH AT!!

SHE THINKS SHE'S *TRICKED* ME WITH HER WHITE FACE AND COLD RED LIPS — AND STRANGE SMILE — I CAN SEE HER *SMILING* — BUT SHE'LL PAY FOR THIS *YET*!!

HIS FACE NOW BRIGHTLY LIT BY THE EVIL LIGHT OF *REVENGE*, STEVE SEEKS TO LOCATE THE PALE GIRL HE HAD ONCE ADORED!

MISS GORDON LEFT HER ADDRESS AS 138 PIEDMONT AVENUE, PARKVILLE.

THANK YOU VERY MUCH!

YES, I'M LAURA'S MOTHER. SHE'S IN THE *GRAVEYARD* NOW — BUT I DON'T UNDERSTAND—

YOU *WILL*—!

SO I'VE *FOUND* YOU AT LAST!! AND IN A VERY APPROPRIATE SETTING, TOO!!

WHO ARE YOU?? WHAT DO YOU WANT WITH *ME*?

SUDDENLY ALL THE BLIND FURY OF *HATRED* AND *FRUSTRATION* IS POURED INTO STEVE'S FINGERS WHICH TIGHTEN ...TIGHTEN ABOUT THE YOUNG GIRL'S THROAT!

DIE!!

NO!! GIRGHH--

LAURA GORDON-- DIED 1942 -- W-WH-- THEN WHO--?? *NO!! NO!!*

LAURA GORDON
BORN 1919
DIED 1942
AGED 22

A NAME ON A TOMBSTONE—AND ALL AT ONCE, THE TERRIBLE TRUTH STRIKES AT A TERRIFIED MURDERER.!!!

LAURA'S BEEN DEAD FOR TEN YEARS! I MUST HAVE KILLED HER TWIN SISTER!

I MUST GET BACK TO MY ROOM! I FEEL AS IF *THEY* WERE *FOLLOWING* ME!

COME, SISTER, HE MUST NOT ESCAPE!

LET US *DANCE* ABOUT HIM 'TIL HE HAS PAID THE PRICE FOR THE *BLOOD* ON HIS HANDS!!

AH-H-H-H!!! GO AWAY!!

DANCE!! ON AND ON AND ON!

I MUST GET OUT OF HERE!

AS THE DAYS PASS, THE HUNTED MAN FLEES MORE AND MORE DESPERATELY FROM THE PALE DANCING FURIES THAT SEEK TO *DESTROY* HIM!

HOW LONG HAVE I BEEN RUNNING? WHEN WILL I MAKE MY PEACE WITH THEM?

HOW DID I GET BACK *HERE*? MAYBE IF I SPEAK TO THEIR *DEAD BODIES*—

OH, WHAT'S THE USE? I'LL NEVER BE FREE OF THEM! *NEVER, NEVER!*

DANCE! DANCE!!

THERE'S ONLY *ONE* ESCAPE FOR ME— AND I MUST *TAKE* IT!

IN THE *SINISTER* STILLNESS OF THE EVENING A GRIM *SHADOW* FALLS ACROSS TWO GRAVES. TWO RESTLESS SPIRITS OF THE DEAD ARE SILENCED *FOREVER* AS STEVE'S BODY DANGLES IN THE FINAL *DANCE OF DEATH!*

LAURA GORDON BORN 1919 DIED 1942 AGE 22

KATHY GORDON BORN 1919 DIED 1951 AGE 32

THE END

MASTER OF EVIL!

OUT OF THE SEARING SMOKE OF SULPHUR HE COMES. TONGUES OF BLUE FLAME SWIRL ABOUT HIS GLISTENING BODY. FEAR PAVES HIS PATH. HE IS THE...

THE BELIEF IN THE DEVIL FOUND FERTILE GROUND IN THE NEW WORLD. THE INDIAN TRIBES WERE DEVIL-WORSHIPPERS AND SUPERSTITIONS DIRECTED MANY ACTIVITIES IN THEIR LIVES.

SOMEWHERE IN NEW ENGLAND, THEY SAY, THERE YAWNS THE *DEVIL'S PIT*. FROM THIS PIT, THE DEVIL RISES AND CALLS TOGETHER ALL THE WITCHES AND SORCERERS OF THE LAND TO PRACTISE THE BLACK ARTS!

THOSE WHO BELIEVE IN THE DEVIL IMAGINE THEMSELVES TO HAVE UNUSUAL POWERS, SUCH AS THE POWERS TO BECOME INVISIBLE, CHANGE THEIR SHAPES AND DESTROY CROPS.

THE WORLD'S LITERATURE IS FULL OF PACTS WHICH HUMAN BEINGS HAVE MADE WITH THE DEVIL. THE DEVIL WOULD PROMISE CERTAIN THINGS TO A PERSON IN EXCHANGE FOR THAT PERSON'S LIFE AFTER A SPECIFIED TIME HAD ELAPSED.

SHE FOUND *IT* HIDDEN IN A *DARK, SECRET CREVICE.* IT SHOWED HER THE WAYS OF THE *EVIL, BLACK ART* THAT WAS THE . . . . .

BOOK OF Vengeance

BOIL, BREW.!! AND SEND YOUR *DEADLY FUMES* ACROSS THE AIR TO KILL, *KILL, KILL.!!* HEHEHEHEHE.!!

ABIGAIL, GET THESE BOOKS TO THE STACKS AND BE QUICK ABOUT IT.!!

YES, MISS SIMMONS. RIGHT AWAY...

WHY IS EVERYONE AGAINST ME? WHAT HAVE I EVER DONE TO THAT WOMAN?

ORIAL LIBRARY

MISS SIMMONS

HER MIND A MIXTURE OF *HATE* AND *FEAR,* ABIGAIL MAKES HER WAY THROUGH THE *GLOOMY* UNUSED STACKS. THEN...

WHY--WHY, A DOOR IS OPENING.! IT OPENED WHEN I TOUCHED THIS DUSTY BOOK ON *WITCHCRAFT!*

CREEEK!

A SECRET ROOM! I--I'M GOING IN. I FEEL I MUST!

INTO THE SECRET ROOM ABIGAIL CREPT SLOWLY, HER MIND FASCINATED BY THE EVIL ASPECT OF THE PLACE...

THIS ROOM MUST HAVE BEEN A WITCH'S DEN... CAN IT GIVE ME REVENGE?

ABIGAIL'S APPEARANCE CHANGES AND HER BRAIN KNOWS ONLY THE SINISTER, BLACK ART OF DEALING CRUEL DEATH...

CHELIDAR, YDARB, MAILLIM...RISE RATS! HELP ME, O EVIL SPIRITS! REVENGE...REVENGE!!

COME, YOU CREATURES OF SEWERS AND GUTTERS!! DO MY BIDDING! NOW, MISS SIMMONS, YOU HAVE WRONGED ME FOR THE LAST TIME... HEHEHEHEHE!!

AT THE BIDDING OF THEIR EVIL MISTRESS, THE SLIMY RODENTS SLOWLY, EVER SO SLOWLY APPROACH THE SOFT, SLEEPING BODY OF THE HEAD LIBRARIAN!

EEEEEEEEK!!! HELP!! HELP!! NO--NOOOOO!!!

HEHEHEHE!! REST WELL, DEAR MISS SIMMONS! HEHEHEHE!!!

WE CAN'T UNDERSTAND *HOW* MISS SIMMONS MET HER TERRIBLE END!

WELL, ABIGAIL, NOW YOU'RE HEAD LIBRARIAN. I HOPE YOU DO AS GOOD A JOB AS...SHE...

PLEASE... (SOB-SOB)... I DON'T WANT TO TALK ABOUT IT! MISS SIMMONS AND I...WE HAD GROWN SO CLOSE TO ONE ANOTHER! (SOB)

REFERENCE ROOM

MISS ROBINS

REVENGE NOW SEARED THE *WARPED MIND* OF ABIGAIL LIKE THE *FLAMING BRANDS* WHICH BURNED THE WITCHES OF OLD. THE DIABOLICAL SCHEME TOOK POSSESSION OF HER *BLACK SOUL!*

NOW, ALLEN KENT, FOR BREAKING *OUR* ENGAGEMENT TO MARRY SOMEONE ELSE, YOU WILL RECEIVE MY *WEDDING GIFT!*

SISTERS OF EVIL, FILL THIS GARMENT WITH THE FIRES OF THE INFERNAL REGIONS THAT IT MAY SEAR THE FLESH OF ALLEN KENT WITH THE FIRES OF DARKNESS –THE SLOW FIRE THAT TORTURES BEFORE CONSUMING!

LOOKS LIKE ANOTHER WEDDING PRESENT, MR. KENT.

THANK YOU, THOMAS. IT SEEMS *EVERYONE* IS WISHING ME WELL!

BUT A FIERY DOOM WAS TO SPOIL THE DAY OF THE NEW BRIDEGROOM.

I...I'M *BURNING UP!* I CAN'T GET THE ROBE OFF... *HELP!!* I...I CAN'T STAND THE *PAIN...*

OH, NO! DARLING, SPEAK TO ME!! WHAT FOUL FIEND CAUSED THIS? ALLEN, DARLING... *HELP!!!*

BUT THERE WAS ONE MORE *EVIL DEED* TO BE DONE! ONE MORE WORK OF NATURE MUST BE *VIOLATED* BEFORE THE *CRAZED* ABIGAIL CAN REST...

OH, MARY, HOW AWFUL FOR YOU.

OH, ABIGAIL, I...I JUST CAN'T BELIEVE IT. IT MUST BE A *NIGHTMARE!* (SOB--SOB)

YES, MY DEAR MRS. KENT, IT IS A NIGHTMARE...OF REVENGE! STEAL ALLEN FROM *ME*, WILL YOU!

EVEN AS IT IS APPLIED THE *VILE VENOM* WITHIN THE FACIAL LOTION BEGINS ITS *SLOW PROCESS*, LIKE *MOLTEN LAVA* INCHING DOWN A *CRAGGY* MOUNTAIN...

I...I HOPE I CAN SLEEP TONIGHT! I'M *SO* WEARY...

...AND INCH BY INCH BURROWING INTO THE SOFT CREVICES OF THE LOVELY FACE, UNTIL...

OH, I FEEL MUCH BETTER. THIS ...*AIEEEEEE!!!* OH, GOD, NO, NO, NO...

MY *DEEDS* ARE ON EVERYONE'S LIPS! MY POWER IS GREAT! IT IS NOW WITHIN ME TO *RULE!!* NO LONGER SHALL I BE DOWNTRODDEN.

AGAIN, IN THE *DARK RECESSES* OF THE *CHAMBER OF EVIL* THE *WITCH* STIRS THE *POTENT BREW*, THIS TIME THE *MADNESS OF POWER* IS UPON HER...

BIRDS OF CARRION, SWARM OVER THE CITY UNTIL YOU HAVE *BLOTTED OUT* THE *LIGHT* OF THE *SUN* WITH YOUR WINGS! BUT DO NOT ACT UNTIL *I* GIVE COMMAND!!

VULTURES... EVERYWHERE YOU LOOK!! WHERE DID THESE *BIRDS OF DEATH* COME FROM??

NOW... *NOW* MY HOUR HAS ARRIVED! I SHALL GIVE THE ORDER FOR THE BIRDS TO *KILL!*

EEEEEEEEK!! I'M ON FIRE! HELP! HELP!!! ARRRGH...

WHEN THE *BRAIN* OF THEIR *FOUL MISTRESS* WAS ENVELOPED BY THE *EVIL FIRE*, THE FESTERING, GHOULISH BIRDS BEGAN TO *BURN*...

SHRIEK!

SHRIEK!

EEEEK!

LOOK! THEY'RE CATCHING ON FIRE!!

THEY...THEY'RE DISAPPEARING!!

THEY'RE GOING UP IN PUFFS OF SMOKE!!

THE CITY IS SAVED...

AGAIN THE CHAMBER IS LOST FROM HUMAN EYES. NOW, HOWEVER IT HAS BECOME A VAULT...A VAULT OF A WITCH! *The End.*

PACT WITH THE DEVIL!

The gaunt trees sagged over the road. Their skeleton-like branches moaned as the night wind moved them back and forth. The whole scene looked as if the devil had thrown his cloak over it! Then . . .

"Move faster, you monster of laziness, or I'll tear the flesh from your back!"

SWASH!!!

Out of the blackness tumbled a horse and carriage. The rider, a coat streaming from his shoulders, was forcing his horse on with booming curses and deadly strokes of a snake whip.

It was Califf Marlowe!

The whip slashed down on the horse's back again. The black fog of night seemed to cringe away as the carriage came on.

"Get on, you lout . . . don't you know that I, Califf Marlowe, the wealthiest man in this county, have been laughed out. Don't you know that they've taken my wealth from me. A crook . . . a disciple of the devil they called me!"

The horse could understand nothing except that it had to escape from those terrible blows. It couldn't understand that Califf Marlowe was the most hated man in the county because he did everything to get power for himself. And the people had revolted and stripped the tryant of his wealth. So it was that Marlowe was on this road plunging homeward to prevent the angry victims of his evil from burning down his house. Suddenly . . .

Out of nowhere there came a blinding flash. The horse reared back, its front paws madly tearing at the air. Califf fell back, his face deeply creased by the sudden, blinding light. Then, all was silent and only a tall man in black stood before the cowering Marlowe.

"Califf," the stranger called, "come here."

Marlowe felt himself powerless, drawn to the man. He had no control over his stumbling feet.

"You called me."

"Yes, Califf. How would you like to have your power back."

"M-My p-power back! I—I . . ."

"You would give your soul for it, wouldn't you!"

"My s-soul, I . . . yes, I would give anything to get back at those who have ruined me."

The stranger pulled his black cloak tightly around himself. "Califf Marlowe, listen to me then! I will give you that power if you promise to give yourself up to me eight years from this very night!"

"Oh, Man in Black, I agree. I promise you you anything for power!"

The night ended. Later, it was discovered that the men going to burn Marlowe's house were killed in a bloody accident. As the months passed, Marlowe's wealth and power began to return. As if by some unseen hand, things happened only for Califf's good. Once again, Marlowe's evil was pressing fear into the hearts of the people.

The years passed. Power and wealth such as Califf Marlowe had never dreamed of came to him. But, the time was up. Eight years had passed. And on a certain night, as Califf counted his gold in his study . . .

"CALIFF . . . CALIFF MARLOWE!"

"W-who called my name? Who is in my room? Who . . . ahhhh . . ."

"Yes, Marlowe, it is I! The Man in Black! Have you forgotten our agreement?"

"A-agreement? What agreement?"

"Don't pretend ignorance, Marlowe. You know what I mean. Come!"

The man in the flowing black cloak approached the trembling Califf.

"No, no! Stay back . . . you, you DEVIL!"

At those words, the stranger threw up his arms and began to chant. Dark shapes flooded the room. The floor fell away and only a deep glowing pit yawned below.

Clammy arms clutched at Califf. Razor-like teeth sunk deeply into Marlowe's flesh.

"Nooooo! Argghhhh . . ."

"Pull him into the pit, oh servants of darkness. He has made a pact with us."

Slowly, the demons dragged the kicking, insane Marlowe to the pit. With a surge, they carried the screaming man over the edge!

The next morning, in the general store . . .

"Bill . . . Joe . . . listen to what I've just heard. Marlowe's house burned down and Marlowe was found BURNED to death in it!"

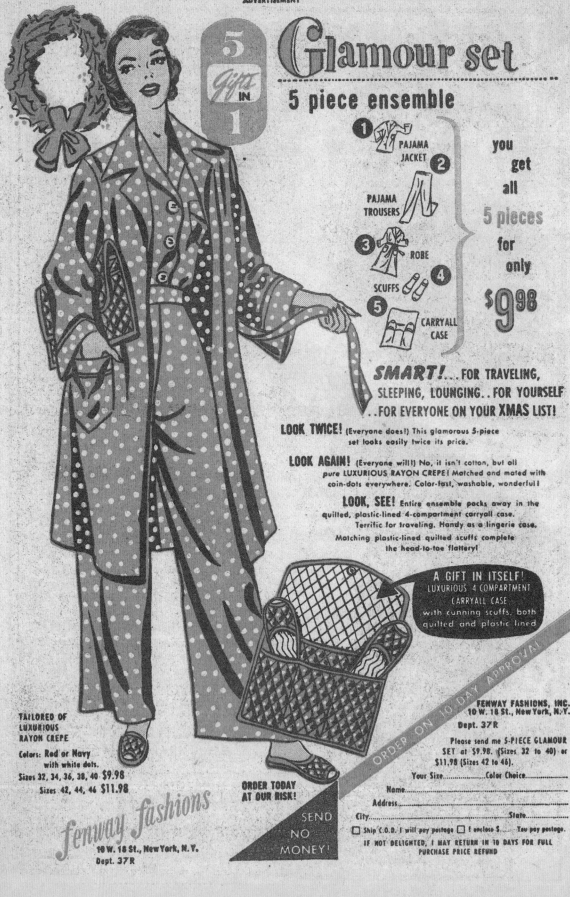

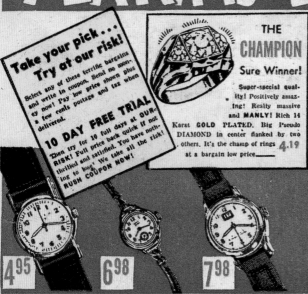

CHAMBER OF CHILLS
TALES OF TERROR AND SUSPENSE
CHAMBER OF CHILLS
MAGAZINE
10¢
PDC
5
FEB.
JIM... JIM... YOU'VE KNOCKED THE STAKE OUT OF HIS HEART!!
WE DARE YOU.... TO OPEN THE MYSTERIOUS DOOR INTO A WORLD OF HORROR!
IN THIS ISSUE!
THE SHRUNKEN SKULL!
OPERATION... MONSTER!

Miss Lee-Fashions

Style #634 MIDNIGHT MIST'RY

Entice him, excite him—exotically veiled in misty marquisette. Glamorous sheer-shadowed shoulders. Devastating decolletage enhances a bewitching buttoned bodice. Twirl in a whirling, wispy skirt . . . adorned with exquisite imported Chantilly lace . . . atop a hip-hugging taffeta slip.

IN BEAUTIFUL COLORS:

- BLACK
- ROSE
- AQUA
- AMERICAN BEAUTY

Imported Chantilly Lace

IN ALL SIZES
9-11-13-15-17
10-12-14
16-18-20

only **9**⁹⁸ _only_ 9^{98}

16½-18½-20½
22½-24½-26½
38-40-42
44-46-48

only **10**⁹⁸

Style #472 NIGHT OF LOVE

Tantalizing lattice lace sweeps extravagantly accross the flesh-tinted dropped shoulder. Dramatic tunic-peplum plunges recklessly to a sculptured train. Luxurious Rayon Faille

IN ALL SIZES only **6**⁹⁸
9-11-13-15-17
10-12-14-16-18-20
16½-18½-20½
22½-24½-26½ only **7**⁹⁸
38-40-42-44-46-48

Send 10¢ for our latest catalog!

IN BEWITCHING COLORS:

- BLACK
- ROYAL BLUE
- PEACOCK
- RED
- COPPER

SENT ON APPROVAL — 10 DAY FREE TRIAL!

MISS LEE-FASHIONS, Inc., Dept. HN
400 Madison Ave., New York 17, N.Y.
Please send me the following dresses in styles, sizes and colors indicated. If not delighted I may return dress within 10 days for refund.

Style No.	Size	First Color Choice	Second Color Choice

☐ Send C.O.D. I enclose $1.00 deposit. I'll pay postman balance plus postage.
☐ I enclose full amount $_____, you pay postage.

NAME _____
ADDRESS _____
CITY _____ ZONE ___ STATE _____

A.P.O. and Foreign Orders must be Prepaid

CHAMBER OF CHILLS MAGAZINE, FEBRUARY, 1952, Vol. 1, No. 5, IS PUBLISHED EVERY OTHER MONTH by WITCHES TALES, INC., 1860 Broadway, New York 23, N.Y. Application for second class entry pending at the Post Office at New York, N.Y. under the Act of March 3, 1879. Single copies 10c. Subscription rates, 10 issues for $1.00 in the U.S. and possessions, elsewhere $1.50. All names in this periodical are entirely fictitious and no identification with actual persons is intended. Contents copyrighted, 1951, by Witches Tales, Inc., New York City.
Printed in the U.S.A.

WON'T YOU COME IN?

The flames of the fantastic leap high in the brimstone pit. Again, the fuels of horror and mystery have been fed them. Again, CHAMBER OF CHILLS takes form.

A-ha-a-a-a, and how you fiends of fury-swept adventure delight in these travels into the realms of the supernatural. Those of the underworld welcome you . . . always!

Ah, the wind begins to moan and the candle atop the skull burns low. The time for entering the CHAMBER OF CHILLS draws near.

However, before we enter, let us mention a few of the letters we have been receiving from you . . . a few of your remarks telling us how excellent CHAMBER OF CHILLS is. Such are the things which fire us with imagination. Such are the things which let us know if we are giving you what you want.

THRILLED AND CHILLED!
I've read them all but your magazine of mystery and suspense is the best yet.
C. B., Chicago, Ill.

STRANGE!
Your stories aren't like others I've read. They make you grip your seat and hang on until the last word. They're so strange and different.
B. T., New York, N. Y.

EXCITING!
After reading your magazine for the first time, I now know what the meaning of "exciting" is.
M. O., Bethlehem, Pa.

THROUGH THE *CRAWLING JUNGLE BEAT* THE *DRUMS* OF THE *LIVING DEAD.* ANCIENT *RITES* ARE PERFORMED BY *FETID CORPSES* GUIDED BY A *WARPED MIND* ENCLOSED IN...

The SHRUNKEN SKULL

TWENTY FIVE DOLLARS! GOING! GOING! GONE..! SOLD TO THE MAN FOR TWENTY FIVE DOLLARS. I HOPE THE *MYSTERY BOX* CONTAINS SOMETHING VERY VALUABLE, SIR...

INTO HIS APARTMENT, MICHAEL STEARNS CARRIED THE SMALL BOX, LITTLE KNOWING THE *UNEARTHLY HORROR* OF ITS CONTENTS! SLOWLY HE UNWRAPPED IT...

TWENTY-FIVE DOLLARS! WHEN WILL I STOP BEING A SUCKER FOR THESE GET-RICH-QUICK SCHEMES OF MINE?

AAAAH!! IT...IT'S A HEAD! A *SHRUNKEN CANNIBAL HEAD!!*

MICHAEL CAST THE *PUTRID, ONCE HUMAN MASS* UPON THE TABLE AND AS HE LOOKED AT IT, IN FEARFUL *FASCINATION,* THE *HORRID* FORM SEEMED TO *PULSATE WITH LIFE...*

THE...THE *HAIR!* IT...IT'S *GROWING!* AND THE *EYES* ARE *BLINKING!!* OH, *NO!!* I MUST BE DREAMING...

SLOWLY, THE *GROTESQUE MOUTH* BEGAN TO OPEN AND SIGH, LIKE THE FLAPPING OF A *MILLION PETULANT BAT WINGS* IN THE FARTHEST CORNER OF HELL! THEN...

MICHAEL STEARNS--- COME CLOSER AND LISTEN TO MY STORY...

NO.!! NO.!! I...I MUST BE GOING MAD!

MANY MOONS AGO I WAS A PRIESTESS IN THE SUGALI TRIBE OF THE ORINOCO HEAD-HUNTERS. BUT I WAS IN LEAGUE WITH THE DEVIL-GOD. I HAD POWERS OF EVIL WHICH MADE MY TRIBESMEN FEAR ME...

MICHAEL'S *HYPNOTIZED MIND* WAS *FORCED* ACROSS THE SEA AND INTO THE *TEEMING* JUNGLES TO WITNESS THE *SATANIC POWERS* OF THE PRIESTESS ...

NO! STOP HER!!! SHE IS TURNING MY SON INTO A *MONSTER!*

SERVANT OF THE DEVIL!! I WILL KILL YOU!!

IT IS DONE! HEHEHE!!! NOW I SHALL RULE WITH MY EVIL POWER... ALL SHALL BOW DOWN TO ME!!

SEIZE HER!!

BRING HER TO THE EXECUTION BLOCK...

FOOLS! KILL ME IF YOU THINK I CAN DIE!! BUT FIRST I PUT THE *CURSE OF LIVING DEATH* UPON YOU ALL! YOU SHALL SLEEP WHILE THE *FLESH ROTS OFF YOUR BONES,* AND YOU SHALL NEVER RISE UNTIL I RETURN AND BID YOU TO DO SO...

THEN SLOWLY MICHAEL'S INCREDULOUS MIND WAS GUIDED BACK TO THE *THING* OF *TERROR* WHOSE *SINISTER SMILE* CONFRONTED HIM...

BUT...BUT HOW DID YOU GET TO AMERICA?

THEN, MICHAEL, THEY SHRUNK MY HEAD AS IS THEIR CUSTOM AND I WAS DISCOVERED BY AN EXPLORER WHO BROUGHT ME HERE. YOU KNOW THE REST. BUT...

...I NEED A BODY UPON WHICH TO PLACE MYSELF. I KNOW YOU, MICHAEL, TO BE GREEDY FOR GOLD, AND I WILL GIVE YOU GREAT WEALTH AND POWER OVER DEATH IN EXCHANGE FOR A BODY FRESHLY DECAPITATED!

YOU-- YOU MEAN YOU WANT ME TO...TO...

THE THOUGHT OF THIS *HORRID PROPOSAL* FILLED MICHAEL WITH *TERROR.* TO *KILL* FOR THIS THING WAS MORE THAN HIS MIND COULD CONTAIN! YET...

YES! I'LL DO IT. POWER AND WEALTH WILL BE MINE. WHAT IS ONE LIFE, ONE *MURDER*...

WAITING, MICHAEL DISCOVERS HIS BEAUTIFUL VICTIM. AND WITH THE *STEALTH* OF A *CRAZED WERE-WOLF,* HIS GREEDY EYES WATCH HER WALK BEFORE HIM...

BUT THE VILLAGE WAS NOT DESERTED. CAVERNOUS EYES WATCHED WITHOUT SEEING—*SKULLS* IN A *DEATH-LIKE SLEEP* OCCUPIED EVERY *FILTHY* HOVEL...

MY *CURSE!* IT WORKED!

SKELETONS!! *EVERYWHERE!* A WHOLE VILLAGE FULL OF THEM...

NOW TO MAKE THE DEAD RISE!! AID ME YOU EVIL SPIRITS AND CREATURES OF THE FOREST... ARRA BIANITES!! SARTORIS ARTISBY MAKAW LEEY!!

DOSID MAGYOSBAT!!

CLICK CLACK

RATTLE

AND THEN, ON THAT *UNHALLOWED* SPOT, APPEARED A SIGHT MORE *HORRIBLE* THAN *DEMON* HAD EVER DEVISED...

OH!! HOW HORRID!!! I MUST GET AWAY. NO POWER OR WEALTH IS WORTH *THIS*...

ACCURSED RACE!!! NOW DO MY BIDDING. *DANCE!!!!* DANCE THE *DANCE OF THE LIVING DEAD!*

DANCE, FOOLS!! HEHEHEHEHE!!!!!

BOOM!
BOOM

THE *MAD, WILD DANCE* OF THE *LIVING DEAD* CONTINUED THRU THE NIGHT, AND THE *MANIACAL THROBBING* OF THE DRUMS CARRIED TO EVERY CORNER OF THE JUNGLE...

BOOM
BOOM
BOOM

THEY...THEY'RE COMING TO HER DEFENSE! NO! STOP!! I'M YOUR FRIEND...SHE WAS EVIL!!! NO!!!

AIEEEEEE!!! L--LET ME GO, YOU FOOL!!!

ARRRGHHHH!!

TIME, WHICH PICKS BONES CLEAN, CLAIMS ANOTHER VICTIM IN THE *VILLAGE* OF *DEATH*. AND, AS THE LAST BIT OF TISSUE FALLS AWAY, A FAINT SMILE SEEMS TO PLAY ABOUT THE MOUTH OF THE *SHRUNKEN HEAD* WHICH LIES NEAR THE *ROTTING CORPSE*...

AND THE DAYS PASSED AS THE MURKY DEPTHS OF THE JUNGLE TRIED TO CONCEAL THE HIDEOUS SCENE OF *TERROR* AND *HORROR*...

THE SILENCE OF THE EVIL VILLAGE REMAINS UNBROKEN UNTIL...

LOOK, SMITH, A VILLAGE...

SEEMS TO BE ONE OF THE SUGALI TRIBES! THIS PROMISES TO BE INTERESTING...

COULD HAVE BEEN A PLAGUE... SO MANY OF THEM!

EASY TO SEE IT WASN'T WAR. THEY'VE ALL GOT THEIR HEADS!

WE OUGHT TO FIND SOMETHING OF VALUE HERE, ANYWAY...

THEN, AS IF PLANNED, THE EVIL SKULL WAS FOUND!!

LOOK! A SHRUNKEN HEAD; THESE ARE VALUABLE. WHAT LUCK!!

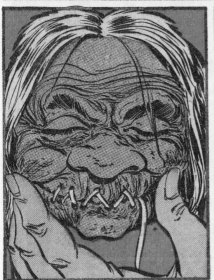

AGAIN THE *SHRUNKEN SKULL* OF THE *PRIESTESS* OF THE *DEVIL* RETURNS TO SEEK NEW *PREY* FOR HER *WARPED LOVE* OF *POWER* AND *VENGEANCE*...

WELL, SMITH - HOME AGAIN! AND WE DO HAVE GOOD CURIOS TO MARKET, DON'T WE?!

YES- BUT YOU KNOW, EVER SINCE WE PICKED UP THAT *HEAD* IN THE DESERTED VILLAGE I'VE FELT *UNEASY!* I'LL BE GLAD WHEN WE'RE RID OF IT!!

FIFTEEN DOLLARS ONCE! FIFTEEN DOLLARS TWICE!! SOLD TO THE GENTLEMAN!!! I'M SURE YOU WON'T BE DISAPPOINTED, SIR!

AUCTION

AND ANOTHER UNSUSPECTING *VICTIM* OF THE *SPIRITS* OF *EVIL* IS TEMPTED BY FATE TOWARD POWER AND OCCULT KNOWLEDGE ...

I CAN HARDLY WAIT TO GET HOME TO SEE WHAT I BOUGHT...

AUC TO SEPTE

THE END

WHEN JACK MALLOY CLIMBED TO THE TOP OF THE BIG TOP TO PERFORM HIS *DEATH DEFYING* FEATS ON THE HIGH TRAPEZE, HE DIDN'T KNOW THAT HE HAD...

AN APPOINTMENT WITH A CORPSE!

OH! HE *MISSED* THE TRAPEZE!

I...I CAN'T WATCH IT!

NO... NO!!

JACK!! JAAAAAAA...!

AS THE FALLING MAN HITS THE FLOOR WITH A *SICKENING THUD*, THE CROWD DOESN'T SEE THE MAN WHO STANDS ABOVE THEM GRINNING EVILLY...

NO ONE WILL EVER KNOW THIS WAS *NOT* AN ACCIDENT! NOW I WILL GET ALL THE HEADLINES INSTEAD OF JUST BEING ALONZO'S ASSISTANT!

HE...HE'S STILL ALIVE! BUT HOW COULD HE...? I MEAN, MAYBE HE STILL HAS A CHANCE!!

JACK, HOW DID IT HAPPEN!? ALONZO HAS BEEN A TOP PERFORMER FOR TEN YEARS AND HE'S NEVER HAD AN ACCIDENT!

SO ALL DID NOT GO ACCORDING TO THE PLAN IN THE *MURDEROUS MIND* OF JACK MALLOY! ALONZO STILL LIVED...

HIS...HIS TIMING WAS JUST A FRACTION OFF, AND YOU KNOW, IN OUR BUSINESS, THAT MEANS *DEATH*!!

POOR GUY--AND *YOU* MUST FEEL AWFUL, BEING HIS PARTNER FOR THREE YEARS! COME ON, LET'S GET DOWN TO THE HOSPITAL...

I'LL JUST SNEAK IN A FEW MOMENTS BEFORE THE OTHERS... I'VE GOT TO SEE IF HE KNOWS ANYTHING...

YOU! I...I'VE BEEN WAITING FOR YOU, JACK! YOU *VIPER*--THE MAN WHO I *THOUGHT* WAS... MY FRIEND! (COUGH-COUGH)

SO YOU DO KNOW I DID IT! WELL, I'M GLAD! I WAS TIRED OF BEING YOUR ASSISTANT!

YOU FOOL... I..I TAUGHT YOU EVERYTHING! MY... MY *CURSE* IS ON YOU, JACK MALLOY... MY *CURSE!!* AAAAAAARGHGGHH... THE PAIN...*THE PAIN!!!*

DIE, ALONZO... *DIE!* THIS TIME I'LL MAKE SURE...! OH, NURSE... UH, YOU'D BETTER HURRY, HE'S VERY BAD...

...HELP... HELP...

HOW DID YOU GET IN HERE? THERE AREN'T SUPPOSED TO BE ANY VISITORS!

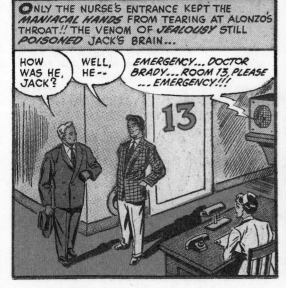

ONLY THE NURSE'S ENTRANCE KEPT THE *MANIACAL HANDS* FROM TEARING AT ALONZO'S THROAT!! THE VENOM OF *JEALOUSY* STILL *POISONED* JACK'S BRAIN...

HOW WAS HE, JACK?

WELL, HE--

EMERGENCY... DOCTOR BRADY... ROOM 13, PLEASE ...EMERGENCY!!!

JACK, I'VE THOUGHT IT OVER AND THE SHOW MUST GO ON! FROM NOW ON I'M GOING TO BILL *YOU* AS OUR GREAT TRAPEZE STAR! WILL YOU GO ON ALONE, TONIGHT?

OF COURSE I WILL... OH, HELLO, JO-JO!

HI, BOSS... HI, JACK! ANY WORD ABOUT ALONZO?

ALONZO The Great!

LAAAADIES AND GENTLE-MEN!!! INTRODUCING JACK MALLOY, WHO IN THE GREAT TRADITION OF ALONZO, WILL PERFORM HIS DEATH DEFYING STUNTS ON THE HIGH TRAPEZE WITHOUT SAFETY NETS!

SOON THEY'LL ALL FORGET ABOUT ALONZO, AND I WON'T HAVE TO SHARE THE SPOTLIGHT EVEN WITH HIS NAME! MAYBE HE'S DEAD ALREADY! I HOPE SO!!

JACK MALLOY FILLED HIS EARS WITH THE THUNDEROUS APPLAUSE OF THE CROWD AS HE PERFORMED THE STUNTS ALONZO TAUGHT HIM! BUT THEN, AT THE VERY END OF THE PERFORMANCE....

MMM... WONDER WHO THAT IS? THE BOSS SAID THIS WAS TO BE A SOLO ACT...!!

AND AS JACK BEGINS HIS LAST STUNT, THE MYSTERIOUS STRANGER SWINGS TOWARD HIM, CLOSER...CLOSER... AND CLOSER, UNTIL WITH FROZEN, BLOODED FEAR, HE SEES...

ALONZO!! WHAT ARE YOU DOING HERE??! NO...NO!! DON'T TOUCH ME!!

KEEP AWAY!! KEEP AWAAAA-AHHHHHHH...

HAH-HAHAHA HAHAHAHAHA HA!

THE GROUND SEEMED TO RUSH UP TO THE FALLING JACK MALLOY WITH THE SPEED OF AN EXPRESS TRAIN! ABOVE HIM HE THOUGHT HE HEARD THE INSANE MUSIC OF A LAUGH WHICH TRAILED AWAY TO A MOURNFUL WAIL...

DID YOU SEE HIM UP THERE? IT...IT...WAS... ALONZO... UHHHH!!

JACK! JACK, THERE'S NO ONE UP THERE...YOU WERE BY YOURSELF! QUICK-GET THE DOC! HE'S OUT!

THIS MAN IS DEAD!! BUT WHAT WAS THAT HE KEPT SAYING ABOUT ALONZO?

ALONZO USED TO BE HIS PARTNER. HE CLAIMED HE SAW ALONZO UP THERE, BUT YOU SEE, THAT WAS IMPOSSIBLE. JUST AFTER JACK WENT UP TO PERFORM THIS EVENING, I GOT WORD FROM THE HOSPITAL THAT ALONZO DIED!!

THE ARMY ANTS

The professor looked up from his maps.

"Wonder what all the noise is?" he thought.

Folding his papers into a case, Professor Albert Jonson stepped out of his tent. It seemed as if the whole jungle were trembling.

"From the sound of those cries, it could be a jungle fire which is disturbing the animals. H-m-m, better get to the top of that rise and see if I can find out what's happening."

Jonson holstered his revolver, slung his rifle over his shoulder and ran to a small hill which looked down into a valley. A man who made many trips into the jungle to study animal and plant life was familiar with the moods of the black jungle. Yet, Professor Jonson felt that this was different. The shrill shrieks and booming bellows of the animals were unlike those he had ever heard before.

Then, Jonson stood atop the hill scanning the countryside. He fell back in amazement!

Below him the jungle seemed to be ripping itself apart. Two-ton elephants were stampeding in entire herds and now seemed as some prehistoric monsters, their heads thrown high... their eyes blazing with terror. Huge cats bounded ahead... their mighty bodies gripped by spasms of horror. Lighter game tumbled about, trying to escape. All living jungle life was trying to get away from... IT!

"Good heavens, I've never seen anything like it. They all are running away from that certain patch of jungle to the south. I must go down there. I must find out what is frightening the animals."

Professor Jonson scrambled down the hill. He circled the place from which all the animals were escaping. As he approached it, he heard a strange crackling noise... as if a gigantic fire were burning. But there was no smoke! Then, he heard the horrible screams of animals which had been trapped inside the area. Suddenly, the answer struck Jonson.

"ARMY ANTS!" The words crashed through his mind. Ants the size of a man's finger were marching through the jungle. The same fear that had gripped the minds of the animals surged through the man's mind. He had to run, too.

As Jonson turned to run, his foot caught on a vine. He fell! When he regained consciousness, minutes later, his eyes bulged from his forehead.

All around him was a red blanket... a red blanket of death whose snapping jaws had already begun to eat away his flesh!

Strange S

To drink water out of the foot-print made by a vicious animal means one can be transformed into that animal... or so certain Europeans believe...

...ORIENT THE OPAL IS THOUGHT ... A GEM OF GOOD FORTUNE ...VENTING ITS WEARER FROM DISEASE AND THE EVIL DESIGNS OF ENEMIES.

...F NEW ...RSTITION ...TCHES STILL ...THE DEVIL AND ...EEDS OF TERROR!

IT IS BELIEVED BY TRIBES DEEP IN THE AFRICAN CONTINENT THAT ONE CAN KILL A PERSON BY TYING KNOTS AROUND VULNERABLE SPOTS ON A DUMMY OF THAT PERSON...

THE DEVIL'S BLOOD

The storm lashed the surrounding country. Gaunt trees sagged under the terrible onslaught by nature. Dirt roads were swallowed up in seas of mud. Lightning whipped the purple skies. Through all this, a lone man plodded along his way.

"Wow, what a mess. Hey, a light!"

The man splashed through the mud as fast as he could. Soon, he was standing before a small shack. He knocked.

"Yes?"

"Sorry to bother you, Mac, but my car broke down and I thought I'd telephone for help. May I use your phone?"

"I have no telephone, but come in. You're very wet and you look tired."

"Yeah, thanks, I might as well."

Inside, the stranger removed his dripping coat and sat down beside a roaring fire.

"Well, this is certainly better. Glad I saw your light."

"I am very glad, also, young man!"

Gil Dobbs looked about the shack. There wasn't much furniture...a table...bed...picture...PICTURE!

"Hey, isn't that the picture of the DEVIL?" gasped Dobbs.

The old man smiled.

"Yes, I painted it myself."

"I hope you don't get offended, but it looks a lot like you now that I come to think of it," weakly grinned Gil.

"Oh, thank you...I mean, it's probably coincidence."

"Some coincidence. The long ears...sharp nose...piercing eyes...just like you've got. Some coincidence."

"Since you're so interested in that picture and the devil, young man, allow me to add to your knowledge of the devil."

For an hour, Gil Dobbs sat spellbound as he listened to lore about the devil. His mind seemed to be in a trance. Then, he heard the old man say, "And through the veins of the devil runs a blue liquid...not red blood. Oh...how careless of me."

The old man had cut himself with a knife he had been handling. The poison of horror flooded Gil's stomach as he saw a blue liquid ooze from the man's finger!

--BUT HIS PULSE IS QUICKENING--- AND HIS FACE IS ODDLY *DISTORTED*... I WOULD SUGGEST---

I AM THE SURGEON IN CHARGE OF THIS OPERATION AND I *WON'T*---

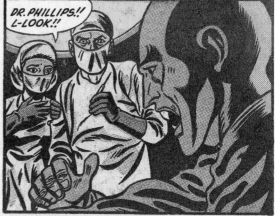

SUDDENLY, THE PATIENT RISES FROM THE TABLE, BUT INSTEAD OF THE *HUMAN BEING* THAT HAD LAIN THERE, A *LOATHSOME HALF-HUMAN* APPEARS, A MONSTROUS CREATION OF THE SURGEON'S KNIFE---

DR. PHILLIPS!! L-LOOK!!

YOUR SCALPEL MUST HAVE TOUCHED THE INNERMOST PART OF HIS BRAIN!! HE'S SOMEHOW BEEN TRANSFORMED INTO A -- A --- *BEAST!!!*

GROWRRR

NOBODY CAN LEAVE HERE *NOW!!* IF OUR HORRIBLE MISTAKE WERE DISCOVERED, THE HOSPITAL WOULD BE *RUINED!!* WE MUST ALL BE SWORN TO SECRECY-- AND *HE* MUST BE HIDDEN AWAY FOREVER!

WHAT SHALL WE DO? WHERE CAN WE KEEP THIS--*MONSTER?*

THERE'S AN *ABANDONED* ROOM ON THE TOP FLOOR-- NOBODY GOES THERE!

IN THE *DEATHLY* QUIET OF THE NIGHT, A STRANGE PROCESSION MOVES, AND EACH WHITE COAT IS A FEARFUL CONTRAST TO THE BLACKNESS OF *EVIL* IN THE HUMAN HEART!...

HURRY! WE'LL BE *SEEN!*

HE HAS THE STRENGTH OF TEN MEN!

AAWRR

THERE!! I HAVE THE KEY AND THE LOCK IS SECURE!

BUT HE'S SO STRONG!! ...I'M AFRAID---

THAT EVENING, IN THE DAMAGED BRAIN OF THE CAGED MONSTER, THERE IS NO RECOLLECTION OF HIS FORMER STATE... NOW THERE IS ONLY SMOULDERING RESENTMENT, BRUTAL ANIMAL INSTINCT...AND TERRIBLE STRENGTH!!

ROWR-RR!! GROWRRR

WITH HANDS GROWN FIERCE AND POWERFUL, THE BEAST RIPS OPEN THE BARS OF HIS HATED PRISON!!...

...AND FRANTICALLY DESTROYS THE DOOR OF THE ROOM...

QUIET PLEASE

CRA SH!

YAAAAAAA

HE'S ESCAPED! I MUST FIND DR. PHILLIPS!!

NURSE! DON'T LEAVE ME HERE!!

HELP!! HELP!!

As the *DEMONIAC* creature continues to stain the halls of the hospital with freshly spilled blood, the police arrive...

CAN'T SOMEBODY *STOP* HIM?!? HIS STRENGTH IS *INHUMAN!*

WE'RE THE ONLY ONES LEFT IN THE HOSPITAL!! THE OTHERS ARE EITHER DEAD -- OR THEY'VE RUN FOR THEIR *LIVES!*

WE *CREATED* THIS *MONSTER,* DOCTOR! IT'S OUR DUTY TO *DESTROY* HIM! MAYBE HE WENT BACK TO HIS ROOM!

I CAN'T SEE VERY WELL -- BUT THE ROOM SEEMS TO BE *EMPTY!*

THEN WE'LL GO INSIDE -- AND *WAIT* FOR HIM TO RETURN!

As the minutes pass, two figures stand in shadow, their eyes piercing the darkness for a glimpse of the terrible *FIEND* they brought into being...

I CAN HEAR THE POLICE BELOW -- SEARCHING FOR HIM!!

WE MUST BE PREPARED TO *KILL* HIM AT ONCE!! THAT NEEDLE IS OUR LAST...

H-HE'S COMING THROUGH THE WINDOW!!... THAT *LOOK* IN HIS EYES -- HOW *HORRIBLE!!* I-I CAN'T MOVE MY ARMS...

DOCTOR, THE NEEDLE! ONLY THAT DRUG CAN STOP HIM!!

GRROWRR

RUN, MISS BAXTER! IN MY FRIGHT, I *DROPPED* THE NEEDLE!

AIEEE!!

LET GO OF ME! YOU *CAN'T* KILL ME!! I---

ARRGHHHHHH

HE'S GOT MISS BAXTER--AND NOW HE WANTS *ME!!!* BUT WHERE CAN I *HIDE??* HE'LL FIND ME *ANYWHERE!!*

LABORATORY 212

GROARR

IF YOU COME NEAR ME, I'LL *CRUSH* YOU WITH THIS METAL WEIGHT! THERE IS STRENGTH IN *ME*, TOO!!

CRACK!

THERE!! WE WILL SEE IF YOUR *INJURED* BRAIN CAN STAND SUCH A BLOW!!

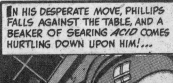

IN HIS DESPERATE MOVE, PHILLIPS FALLS AGAINST THE TABLE, AND A BEAKER OF SEARING *ACID* COMES HURTLING DOWN UPON HIM!...

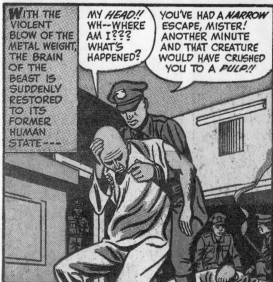

SPIRIT IN THE STONE

After the thing fell from the skies, one man dreamed of good, the other of evil... but neither man had reckoned with the consequences of tinkering with that horrible life force...

Wh...YAAAA...THE METEOR'S C-CRACKING APART AND T...THE R-ROCKS! T-THEY'RE COMING AFTER ME! THE ROCKS ...T... THEY'RE...ALIVE!

HUNGRY? SURE, I'M HUNGRY! BUT NOT FOR YOUR SO-CALLED COOKING! I'M HUNGRY FOR LIFE, FOR LIVING, FOR ALL THE GOOD THINGS OUTSIDE!

EASY, JACK! YOUR NERVES! REMEMBER, WE'RE SCIENTISTS! WE'RE HERE TO HELP HUMANITY!

HUMANITY? BAH! A LOT ANYONE CARES!

THINK OF OUR WORK, JACK, OUR METEOROLOGICAL OBSERVATIONS! WAIT! THE AUTOMATIC METER ALARM IS RINGING!

BRR-RRNNGGGGG

AN INTERSTELLAR BODY— IT'S PASSING THE EARTH'S ATMOSPHERE! AND THE ALARM'S GETTING LOUDER! THAT MEANS THE BODY'S BIG!

I HOPE IT'S BIG ENOUGH TO CRASH THIS ROTTEN PLANET TO ATOMIC DUST! LET IT COME!

G-GOOD GRIEF, IT C-CAN'T BE...! A METEOR... BIG AS THE MOON— AND... IT'S NOT PASSING BY, JACK! IT'S GOING TO CRASH!

J-JACK... OHH!

DOC... YAAAA!

J-JACK! JACK, CAN Y-YOU HEAR ME?

I...I HEAR YOU, DOC! (GASP)...GUESS I'M SHAKEN UP!

I...IT'S UNCANNY... AS...AS IF I SOMEHOW CAUSED IT, WITH MY BLASPHEMY ON SCIENCE!

SKIP IT, JACK! LET'S GO OUTSIDE FOR A LOOK!

MAN, OH MAN, WHAT A BREAK! LOOK AT THE SIZE OF IT! IT'S THE SCIENTIFIC FIND OF THE CENTURY!

IT ALMOST BROKE US, ALL RIGHT! OKAY...I'M COMING!

RETURN OF THE WEREWOLF!

"Do you think *it* will come, tonight?"

Inspector Wilson looked at the full, blood-red moon. "The time is right!"

"It" was the werewolf!

Both men moved uneasily. They were pressed against a boulder and the cold, harsh wind from the moors cut into their bare faces. The large house that rose before them was black...bleak.

Assistant Inspector Hawkins thought about this amazing case. Three months ago, strange, horrible murders began happening on the moors. People returning home late at night were set upon by some vicious beast. Those who lived swore it was a wolf.

Then, the superstitions of the moors began to be revived. Ever since they had come to the moors, the Wellington family was suspected of being cursed by some terrible sickness. All of the male members of the family were never allowed to walk about alone at certain times of the month. Then, two weeks ago, evidence was uncovered which showed that the murdering beast used the Wellington house as its lair. It took but a few days before the werewolf curse became alive on whispering lips.

So, the two police officers had decided to watch the house and see if any strange creature ventured forth from its forboding walls to wreak horrible death.

"Hawkins...Hawkins, can't you hear me? What's the matter with you?" snapped Inspector Wilson.

"Oh, I'm sorry, sir, just thinking about this blasted case. What's up?"

"Didn't you see a light upstairs?"

"No, sir, that house still looks like a tomb to me!"

Hours passed.

The moors looked like some other planet in the white, ghostly moonlight.

The moon was full.

"Hawkins, did you hear something behind us?"

"Yes sir. I'll go back and investigate."

Filmy clouds passed over the moon.

"Aiiieeeehhhhh..."

"Hawkins...HAWKINS...ANSWER ME."

Inspector Wilson tore himself from his position and plunged in the direction Hawkins had gone.

"Good Lord, no!"

Bending over Hawkins' slashed body was... A WOLF!

"Arrghh...arrghhh..."

"Keep away from me, you monster...keep away..."

BANG! BANG! BANG!

"The bullets can't hurt it. I-I must run...I..."

"ARRGHHH..."

"Aiieeeehhhh..."

The monster melted away in the blackness.

Minutes later, a hairy shape began to climb up one of the walls of the Wellington house. When it reached the second floor, it disappeared through a window and was seen no more.

The moon was sinking rapidly behind the barren mounds of the moors. The twisted trees offered a grotesque welcome to the approaching dawn. The wind moaned over two still warm corpses.

On the second floor of the Wellington house, John Wellington III rolled over on his back as the first rays of dawn flooded the room. As the sun touched him, he seemed to snap out of the stupor of sleep. He quickly got up and looked down at the floor.

The muddy prints of some horrible beast led to his bed!

Then, as if he had been doing it over and over again, he wiped up the mud. Afterwards, he ran some water in the bathtub.

He was going to wash fresh mud from his bare feet!

Ghosts THAT NEVER REST!

Aye, mates and lassies, there are ghosts that never die but just walk forever following a tortured path which leads nowhere! Such is the story of...

THE DEVIL-DOOMED SAND-MAN!

HARRY MAIN WAS HIS NAME WHEN HE WAS ALIVE, AND NO BLACKER A MAN DID LIVE! HE RAVAGED THE NEW ENGLAND COAST WITH HIS ACTS OF PIRACY!

THEN, MAIN TURNED TO BEING A WRECKER. HE BUILT FIRES ON THE SANDS TO DECOY VESSELS AMONG THE BREAKERS AND WRECK THEM.

BUT, ONE DAY, THE MURDERER WAS FINALLY CAUGHT AND CHAINED ON THE BEACH.

THE DOG DESERVES NO BETTER!

THAT NIGHT, A RIPPING STORM HIT THE NEW ENGLAND COAST. THE PEOPLE FROZE IN THEIR HOMES WHEN THEY HEARD MAIN'S SHOUTING RISE ABOVE THE HOWLING GALE!

AIEHH! LOOSEN MY BONDS. A CURSE ON YOU ALL!

EVEN TODAY THERE ARE NEW ENGLANDERS WHO STILL CLAIM TO SEE HARRY MAIN'S GHOST WALKING THE SHORE AND WAILING FOR HIS SINS. AND, EVERY TIME HE WALKS, A STORM RAGES!